PHYSICS UNIFIED

PHYSICS UNIFIED

BY

HAROLD ASPDEN

Doctor of Philosophy of Trinity College
in the University of Cambridge

SABBERTON PUBLICATIONS
P.O. Box 35, Southampton, England

ISBN 0 85056 009 8 (Cloth Edition)
ISBN 0 85056 010 1 (Paper Edition)

First published October 1980

Printed and bound in Great Britain at
The Camelot Press Ltd, Southampton

DEDICATION

To my wife, Wendy, for her
patient and enduring support

Contents

Introduction

This book supersedes the author's 1969 *Physics without Einstein* and records the substantial progress of the past ten years in developing the basic theme of that work. Simply stated, the experimental support for Einstein's theory is no proof that his philosophical methods are valid, especially if new physics can provide a broader unified basis for the same observations. A structured vacuum determining universal physical constants is shown in the following pages to be fully compatible with formulae derived by Einstein from his Theory of Relativity. Creation processes on both a cosmic and an atomic scale and the many topics evident from the list of contents are embraced by this unification of fundamental physics. Some of the new material in this book has been published in recent issues of scientific journals but there is much that has not been published hitherto that is of major importance to the author's thesis. It is hoped that the reader will be greatly interested by this new perspective of the physics governing our universe.

1

Unified Field Theory

The Challenge of the Unified Field

On September 10, 1948, Albert Einstein wrote a foreword for a book* by Lincoln Barnett entitled *The Universe and Dr. Einstein.* This foreword concluded with the words:

> The growth of our factual knowledge, together with the striving for a unified theoretical conception comprising all empirical data, has led to the present situation which is characterized—notwithstanding all successes—by an uncertainty concerning the choice of the basic theoretical concepts.

Quoting from the 1966 edition of this work, one reads:

> Dr. Einstein, long professor emeritus at the Institute for Advanced Study in Princeton, spent the last years of his life working on a problem which had baffled him for more than a quarter of a century. This was his Unified Field Theory, which attempted to set forth in one series of mutually consistent equations the physical laws governing two of the fundamental forces of the universe, gravitation and electromagnetism. . . . 'The idea that there are two structures of space independent of each other, the metric-gravitational and the electromagnetic,' Einstein once observed, 'is intolerable to the theoretical spirit.' Yet despite all his efforts he could not incorporate electromagnetic field laws into General Relativity.

Today, as we progress through the 1980s, the pursuit of a viable Unified Field Theory is as elusive as ever. One might well question whether the quest defies solution. Perhaps we have been wrong to prejudge that unification of electrodynamic and gravitational force relationships will emerge from analysis relying strictly on the field

* L. Barnett, *The Universe and Dr. Einstein*, William Morrow, New York, 1966.

concept. Note that in the above quotations Einstein did not use the word 'field'. Those involved in the early study of electrodynamics were very careful to treat their subject empirically, guided by measurements of interaction forces between currents in closed electrical circuits. The concept of a field was merely a consequence of the theoretical interpretation of a restricted range of experimental data. There were no measurements of the electrodynamic interaction forces between discrete charged particles in motion.

Certainly, the electric field associated with the electrostatic interaction formulated in Coulomb's Law, though only notional, seems real enough, because the lines of flux portraying the electric field radiate from the electric charge. However, the notional magnetic field lines we associate with moving charge form closed loops in space remote from the charge itself (see Fig. 1). One should, therefore, be a little less confident as to the reality of such fields in the surrounding void.

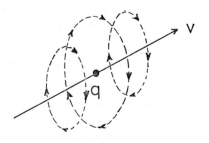

Fig. 1

Nevertheless, the overwhelming success of Maxwell's work on field theory and the fact that Maxwell's equations stand firm under relativistic analysis have secured confidence in the universality of the field concept. The Special Theory of Relativity has been accepted as a unification of field theory so far as electricity and magnetism are concerned and this leads us to hope that the remaining challenge of discovering the onward unification with gravitational theory will emerge from research involving relativistic field concepts.

Be this as it may, the fact that others have been unable to find the connection has led the author to explore an avenue along different lines. It seems best to make a detour around the field concept and concentrate on the unification of electrodynamic and gravitational force relationships, without reference to fields. The problem is rather formidable, for two reasons. First, it requires us somehow to relate Newton's direct inverse-square of attraction law of gravitation with a law of electrodynamics which does not, in general, give a force acting directly along the line between two interacting charges. Second, we have to seek unification, not with the simple law of Isaac Newton, but with the more complex law of gravitation deduced from Albert Einstein's General Theory of Relativity. Einstein's law of gravitation does, however, give a force along the line joining two interacting bodies.

Our object in this chapter is to show first how the electrodynamic force can be formulated on the basis of experimental data so as to be compatible with Newton's Law of Gravitation. Also, we will explore an aspect of inverse-square laws in general, which will allow us to encompass Einstein's law of gravitation. A unification of form between electrodynamics and gravitation will emerge in Chapter 2. Then, given this, the task of justifying a physical link between electrodynamics and gravitation comes into sight and with it the broader objectives of this book, a more unified account of fundamental physics.

The Electrodynamic Force

Merely by taking full account of the conservation of energy there are certain general aspects of the force which acts on a charged particle in motion, bearing in mind that the force is taken to be directed according to the polarity of the charge and the velocity of the charged particle.

Referring to Fig. 2, imagine two electric particles of charge q, Q and mass m, M moving at constant velocity $\mathbf{v}$, $\mathbf{V}$, respectively and subject to a mutual force $\mathbf{F}$ acting directly between them along their

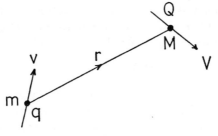

Fig. 2

line of separation. **r** is the separation distance vector from q to Q. Note that we intend to make no reference to the magnetic field as portrayed by the closed lines encircling the velocity vector **v** of the charge q in Fig. 1.

Consider next the energy deployment as charge Q moves under the action of a force **F** acting in the direction $-\mathbf{r}$. This is depicted in Fig. 3. Note that force is itself a concept, when considered alongside truly physical parameters such as energy, mass, distance and time. Force is merely a manifestation as energy is transferred with the changing state of a system. Without energy transfer there is no force,

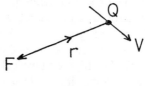

Fig. 3

because force in this constant velocity situation is a rate of change of energy with position.

If the interaction depicted in Fig. 2 is considered as exclusively electrodynamic, meaning that the two velocities **v** and **V** are both constant, there are certain constraints on the electrodynamic inter-action force. We cannot have the charge Q moving at a constant velocity **V** solely under the action of force **F**. The force **F** expends work at a rate expressed by the scalar product $(\mathbf{F.V})$ and the energy has to go somewhere. We might expect **V** to change, but we are considering what has to happen if **V** does not change, that is the circumstance prevailing if there are energy transfer processes at work within the electrodynamic system itself.

Clearly, if force is a consequence of energy seeking a home to assure conservation, Nature asserts another force on Q. Denote this force **Z**, as shown in Fig. 4. We then know that:

$$(\mathbf{F.V}) + (\mathbf{Z.V}) = 0 \tag{1}$$

The interesting point we now focus upon is that, whereas **F** acts through the centre of gravity of the two-body system formed by q and Q, the force **Z** must exert a turning moment on Q about the centre of gravity. **Z** cannot act through this centre because, if it did, then to

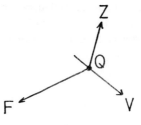

Fig. 4

satisfy (1) it would merely cancel **F** completely and then there would be no electrodynamic action to consider.

Now, as with any self-contained electrodynamic system, we know that the two-body system q, Q cannot acquire angular momentum by virtue of its own self-interaction. This is well established and applied, as will be described later in this work, in interpreting the measurement of gyromagnetic properties in magnetized pivotally-mounted rods when the direction of the intrinsic ferromagnetism is reversed. Angular momentum is conserved as between the rod and the electron motion to which the ferromagnetic state is ascribed.

Historically, there was an experiment in which self-action of currents in a closed circuit was taken to cause rotation.* Writing about it, its author Gore (1875) commented:

These experiments produce a striking effect in a lecture, because rotation appears to be produced without reaction of the moving parts of the apparatus upon any external or fixed body.

Professors Maxwell and Stokes are, however, on record as having challenged Gore and pointed to a weakness in his experimental set-up. Once remedied, the effect did not occur. Hence, the inability of an electrodynamic system to develop rotation by self-action is fundamental and well accepted.

To balance the turning action of **Z** there has to be a third force acting on Q. This third force **P** is an extraneous force arising by reaction. As is usual with reaction phenomena, the reaction force is that associated with a maximization of energy transferred, corresponding to a minimization of potential energy in the primary action. Thus, for optimum reaction involving maximum energy transfer as Q is displaced, the force **P** has to be in the line of the velocity vector **V**.

* G. Gore, *Proceedings of the Royal Society*, **24**, 121 (1875).

So, our argument about energy exchanges and balance leads us to imagine that there are three forces acting on both q and Q, as depicted in Fig. 5. The counterparts of **Z** and **P** at q are denoted **Z′** and **P′**, respectively.

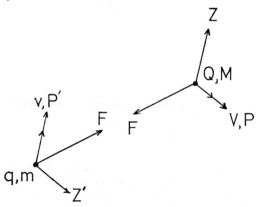

Fig. 5

Fig. 5, as drawn, now suggests the most important step in this analysis. We are seeking to explain electrodynamic action as a direct interaction along the lines joining q and Q, that is, solely in terms of **F**. Yet we know that this primary action is complicated by reaction forces **Z**, **P**, **Z′** and **P′**. What is the condition that the separation vector between q and Q should be unaffected by the motion of the system in response to these four reaction forces? The answer simply is that **Z** and **P** must combine to assert a force on M that accelerates it exactly as m is accelerated by the combination of **Z′** and **P′**, and these four forces must assert no turning couple on the system. The fact that the electrodynamic self-action produces no turning couple is a consequence of the basic requirement that the separation vector **r** is governed solely by the mutual electrodynamic interaction force **F**.

When formulated, the condition just deduced leads to:

$$\mathbf{Z} = (M/m)\mathbf{P′} \qquad (2)$$
and
$$\mathbf{Z′} = (m/M)\mathbf{P} \qquad (3)$$

Z is parallel to **P′** and **Z′** is parallel to **P**.

If we knew **F**, we could, from (1), (2) and (3), derive the complete law of force applicable to the interaction between q and Q. The derivation of **F** is, therefore, the next task.

The Neumann Potential

The electrodynamic action is characterized by a reversal of force when the current of either interacting circuit element reverses. Also, as was known to Ampère as long ago as 1825, the electrodynamic forces exerted by one circuit on another are independent of the linear dimensions of the circuits and so, from dimensional analysis, the force must vary as the inverse-square of separation distance. For an interesting commentary on this see the book by Tricker (1965).* These facts alone allow us to deduce the form of the electrodynamic interaction force **F**.

The system of the two charges q, Q shown in Fig. 2 can be resolved vectorially into nine component interacting systems, with **r** drawn along the x axis in an x, y, z set of co-ordinates. Thus each of the components v_x, v_y, v_z of velocity **v** interacts separately with each of the components V_x, V_y, V_z of velocity **V**.

There are four types of interaction and we consider each below.

Firstly, the action for which the two velocities are mutually orthogonal and one lies along the separation vector, as shown in Fig. 6. If

Fig. 6

there is a mutual balanced interaction force acting between q and Q then it must reverse in direction if the velocity of Q reverses. Yet if the velocity of Q reverses we have but the same system when viewed in reverse direction from behind. Accordingly, by symmetry, the force cannot reverse and so must be zero, since we know it has to be proportional to the velocity if it exists at all.

Secondly, the action for which the two velocities are mutually orthogonal and orthogonal with respect to the separation vector, as shown in Fig. 7. The velocity of q is directed normal to the plane of the figure.

Here, if there is mutual balanced interaction force between q and Q then a related potential energy will be associated with the state depicted in Fig. 7. This energy should be the same however the state comes about. It will be proportional to the product of the two

* R. A. R. Tricker, *Early Electrodynamics*, Pergamon, p. 181, 1965.

velocities in the state shown. Imagine that q travels at high speed and
Q at low speed, to create the state in Fig. 7. During its travel q has
velocity components, one of which is orthogonal to the separation
vector and the other of which is directed along the separation vector.
Motion orthogonal to the separation vector involves no work against

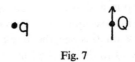

Fig. 7

the mutual force deemed present in the Fig. 7 system. Motion along
the separation vector involves no work because we have seen that the
force is zero in the Fig. 6 system. Hence no work is expended in
creating the Fig. 7 configuration from two well-separated charges. It
follows that the electrodynamic interaction depicted in Fig. 7 has no
energy and that there is no force between q and Q.

The above argument is more readily understood by reference to
Fig. 8, which depicts the charge q progressing rapidly in a direction
orthogonal to the motion of Q, the latter being directed normal to
the figure. Note that if we were considering current flow along
circuit elements, the circuit could be configured as drawn in Fig. 8.

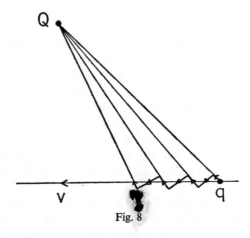

Fig. 8

As can be seen, segments along the flow path of q correspond alter-
nately to systems of the kind shown in Figs. 6 and 7, respectively.

The third action is that depicted in Fig. 9 and the fourth that shown in Fig. 10. The problem is that of relating the mutual balanced interaction force deemed present in the two systems. Let the force in

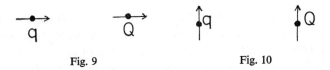

Fig. 9   Fig. 10

Fig. 9, measured in the mutually-attractive sense, be taken as $aqQvV$ at unit spacing and the force in Fig. 10 as $bqQvV$ at unit spacing. Apply these expressions to the charge configuration shown in Fig. 11.

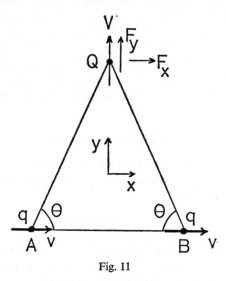

Fig. 11

Here charge Q moves very rapidly at a velocity V away from a symmetrical system of two charges q moving laterally at velocity v in the same plane. Let the force on Q attributable to the combined effect of q at A and q at B have components F_x and F_y, as shown. The force F_x does no work, inasmuch as Q moves in the direction y. The forces F_x and F_y are each the sum of four force components based upon a resolution of each of the q–Q interactions into two of the systems of the form shown in Figs. 9 and 10. Interactions of the form shown in Fig. 6 have been ignored, since the interaction force has been shown to be zero.

It may then be verified that, taking the q–Q spacing as unity:

$$F_x = qQvV\{(b-a)\cos^2\theta\sin\theta + (b-a)\cos^2\theta\sin\theta\} \qquad (4)$$
$$F_y = qQvV\{(b-a)\cos\theta\sin^2\theta - (b-a)\cos\theta\sin^2\theta\} \qquad (5)$$

Evidently, F_y is zero. Also, since F_x does no work either, then the electrodynamic potential of the system is independent of the presence of Q. This means that the electrodynamic forces on the charges q arising from Q must equally do no work. Yet the force $-F_x$ acts in opposition to the motion of the q charges and is shared between them. If this force is finite work must be done as the charges q travel at velocity v. Clearly, therefore, we must conclude that F_x is also zero. This necessitates acceptance that $a=b$. In other words, the interactions of the systems of Figs. 9 and 10 are identical.

Reverting now to the analysis of the general interaction shown in Fig. 2 and the nine interaction components in the resolved system, we find that six of these are zero interactions of the form shown in Figs. 6 or 7. One is of the form shown in Fig. 9 and two have the form shown in Fig. 10. The total interaction force, expressed in the resolved velocity components, is:

$$F = aqQ(v_xV_x + v_yV_y + v_zV_z)/r^2 \qquad (6)$$

Since this force is an attractive force, by assumption, and is acting along the line of the separation vector $\mathbf{r}$, we can write (6) in scalar product notation, thus:

$$\mathbf{F} = -aqQ(\mathbf{v}.\mathbf{V})\mathbf{r}/r^3 \qquad (7)$$

If this is written in current element form by putting $Q\mathbf{V} = i\mathbf{ds}$ and $q\mathbf{v} = i'\mathbf{ds}'$ and a is put as unity, this expression becomes, when integrated as a potential, the Neumann Potential:

$$-ii'(\mathbf{ds}.\mathbf{ds}')/r \qquad (8)$$

This is the classical energy potential associated with the electrodynamic action. i and i' denote currents in circuit elements $\mathbf{ds}$, $\mathbf{ds}'$ separated by a distance r. The fact that two parallel current circuits mutually attract when the currents flow in the same direction determines the sign of the expression and justifies the assumption that a is positive. The unity value of a is merely set by the choice of units.

The Law of Electrodynamics

Having established the form of the force $\mathbf{F}$, we are now ready to formulate the full law of electrodynamics. Write $\mathbf{F}$ as:

$$\mathbf{F} = -K(\mathbf{v}.\mathbf{V})\mathbf{r} \qquad (9)$$

where:
$$K = qQ/r^3 \qquad (10)$$

From (1) and (9), the force $\mathbf{Z}$ in Fig. 5 is given by:

$$-K(\mathbf{v}.\mathbf{V})(\mathbf{V}.\mathbf{r}) + (\mathbf{Z}.\mathbf{V}) = 0$$

Hence:
$$\mathbf{Z} = K(\mathbf{V}.\mathbf{r})\mathbf{v} \qquad (11)$$

Conversely, bearing in mind that $\mathbf{F}$ acting on q is reversed:

$$\mathbf{Z}' = -K(\mathbf{v}.\mathbf{r})\mathbf{V} \qquad (12)$$

From (3) and (12):
$$\mathbf{P} = -K(M/m)(\mathbf{v}.\mathbf{r})\mathbf{V} \qquad (13)$$

The total force acting on Q in Fig. 5 is, therefore, $\mathbf{F} + \mathbf{Z} + \mathbf{P}$, which is, from (9), (10), (11) and (13):

$$\mathbf{F_Q} = (qQ/r^3)\{(\mathbf{V}.\mathbf{r})\mathbf{v} - (M/m)(\mathbf{v}.\mathbf{r})\mathbf{V} - (\mathbf{v}.\mathbf{V})\mathbf{r}\} \qquad (14)$$

This is the complete and general law of electrodynamics to which we have been led by straightforward analysis. It will form the basis of the unified field approach presented in this work.

Electrodynamics has developed empirically from the measurement of interactions between electrons moving at low speeds in closed current circuits. If we put $M = m$ and $q = Q$ in (14) to signify action between identical charge carriers, the law simplifies. It reduces to a simple inverse-square law of mutual attraction for actions between like polarity charges moving mutually parallel. Then the first two terms in (14) cancel to leave the last term in the simplified form:

$$\mathbf{F} = -(q^2/r^3)(\mathbf{v}.\mathbf{V})\mathbf{r} \qquad (15)$$

This establishes the form of law we seek for correspondence with Newton's Law of Gravitation. But is the electrodynamic law, as applied to electron flow in circuits, viable?

The answer to this is that it simply has to be, because we have relied upon the principle of energy conservation in deriving it, and little else. To establish that we are correct, let us digress into the history of the subject.

During the course of the nineteenth century the interaction of currents in electrical circuits was fully explored. The idea that such interactions were collective effects of charged particles, all interacting in some way, was well in evidence. Even though the electron was not isolated for direct measurement of its behaviour in a magnetic field until late in the century, the theory of electricity and magnetism recognized the need for a law of electrodynamics between two isolated charges. We see Maxwell in his great treatise discussing the force which one isolated current element exerts on another.

He presented the most general law of electrodynamic action consistent with the experimental facts. The problem was to formulate the effect of a current i' in a circuit element ds' upon a current i in a circuit element ds. He deduced that the general law would have three components. With r as the separation distance between two elements, his formulation showed that there was a primary force along this line joining the elements and two components of force, one parallel with ds and one parallel with ds'.

The only uncertainty arose because the experimental data invariably included a closed circuit current and this left one parameter (Maxwell termed it Q) uncertain. All he knew was that Q was a function of the separation distance r. Quoting from the third edition of the treatise (Maxwell, 1891):*

> Since the form and value of Q have no effect on any of the experiments hitherto made, in which active current is always a closed one, we may, if we please, adopt any value of Q which appears to us to simplify the formulae.

Now, surely, Maxwell was not here saying that the law of electrodynamics can be left to arbitrary choice. He was saying that *temporarily*, until the future gives us clarifying experimental evidence, we can get by by any convenient choice of Q. Therefore, in the meantime, we may just as well make life easy for ourselves and choose a value for Q which simplifies the formulae. The Biot–Savart version adopted by Lorentz has proved to be the easiest to use. It is a two-stage force relationship linking the two current elements by a common magnetic field parameter. It may be formulated thus:

$$\mathbf{H} = i'\int_{s'}(1/r^3)[\mathbf{ds'}.\mathbf{r}] \tag{16}$$

$$\mathbf{F} = i[\mathbf{ds}.\mathbf{H}] \tag{17}$$

* J. C. Maxwell, *A Treatise on Electricity and Magnetism*, Dover Edition (1954), New York, p. 174 (1891).

However, this vector product version relating field **H** and force **F** was not suggested by Maxwell. He recited four alternative choices of Q, one which gave the law of Ampère, one which gave the above law in quaternion form (Grassmann's law) and two of his own making. After presenting them he opted in favour of Ampère's version, even though this was more complicated, because it was:

undoubtedly the best, since it is the only one which makes the forces on the two elements not only equal and opposite but in the straight line which joins them.

It was here that Maxwell missed an important opportunity. He had thus ignored one of his own proposed laws for which Q was simply $-1/r$ and which gave him the equally-simple force components:

$$(ii'dsds'/r^2)\cos\varphi \quad \text{along } r$$

$$-(ii'dsds'/r^2)\frac{dr}{ds'} \quad \text{along } ds$$

$$+(ii'dsds'/r^2)\frac{dr}{ds} \quad \text{along } ds' \tag{18}$$

φ is the angle between ds and ds'.

What Maxwell failed to recognize was that the most general law of electrodynamics is not one which applies to two electric charges in isolation. If there were only two interacting electric charges in the whole universe they would have to move about one another in elliptical (or circular) motion or would be moving towards or away from one another in a common line. They would always be moving parallel or anti-parallel. In such a situation Maxwell's law in (18) would satisfy the same condition as Ampère's law, that the forces between the charges would be equal and opposite and directed along the line joining them. However, it would be better than Ampère's law, because the force would have the simple inverse square of distance form. The magnitude of the force would be independent of the direction of r in relation to that of the charge velocities. It would be a law resembling Newton's Law of Gravitation in that there would be mutual attraction between like current elements.

Furthermore, since in the general case the interaction force of two charges is merely a component of multiple interactions due to the presence of numerous other charges in motion, we need not be bound to the balance of action and reaction for each such component. There can be complete conformity with Newton's Third Law of Motion for the aggregate effect of a system of charge satisfying any of the possible formulations of the component law. Of course, the component law must, as just indicated, remain the same and be valid in the ultimate situation of two isolated charges moving under their mutual interaction.

Maxwell had himself formulated the law. He failed to see its significance and opted for the Ampère version.

He had introduced his third law of electrodynamics with the words:

> We might, if we pleased, assume that the attraction between two elements at a given distance is proportional to the cosine of the angle between them. In this case $Q = -1/r$.

Note then that this assumption by Maxwell is exactly the form we have deduced for the force $\mathbf{F}$, as given by (9). The force is simply $-(\mathbf{v}.\mathbf{V})/c^2$ times the Coulomb interaction force. Here, we have introduced the speed of light parameter c to convert the electromagnetic units of charge into electrostatic units.

Maxwell's third law of electrodynamics must therefore be the correct empirical law for interaction between the charge carriers in normal electric circuits, that is for interactions between electrons. In vector notation it has the form:

$$\mathbf{F_s} = \frac{ii'}{r^3}\{(\mathbf{ds}.\mathbf{r})\mathbf{ds'} - (\mathbf{ds'}.\mathbf{r})\mathbf{ds} - (\mathbf{ds}.\mathbf{ds'})\mathbf{r}\} \tag{19}$$

When integrated over a closed path to express the action of an element $i'\mathbf{ds'}$ on the complete circuit s carrying current i, the middle term in (19) vanishes. The remaining terms then combine to become:

$$\mathbf{F_s} = \frac{ii'}{r^3}\left[\mathbf{ds}.[\mathbf{ds'}.\mathbf{r}]\right] \tag{20}$$

which is the Lorentz law of force.

The expression (19) is, as expected, of the form we found in (14) when the latter applies to actions between electrons. We find, therefore, that even from the classic work of Maxwell the law of electrodynamics is supported experimentally.

However, we must remember that the law of electrodynamics applies between two charges in motion and, in general, there will be numerous charges involved in electrodynamic interactions. The law applies to all combinations of charge pairs in the system and they all share the same electromagnetic reference frame. The velocities of the interacting charges are measured relative to this frame. It is a non-rotating frame, consistent with the inability of the electrodynamic interaction to generate a turning action and exchange angular momentum with the interacting charges. On the other hand, as we see from Fig. 5, the individual charge interactions can, owing to the electrodynamic action, develop an out-of-balance linear force, seemingly asserted by the electromagnetic frame itself. Such non-compliance with Newton's Third Law of Motion is also apparent from the Biot–Savart or Lorentz law. This is a well discussed theme in the literature on electrodynamics and it does not mean that there will be any net out-of-balance force when such forces are summed for a whole system of charge.

Indeed, Newton's Third Law of Motion is strictly valid only when applied to a complete system. When currents flow in interacting closed, and therefore complete, circuits, the mutual forces comply fully with this law of action and reaction balance. Even in the incomplete system, such as the general arrangement of two moving charges shown in Fig. 5, there may be more than the mere interacting charge present. Some authors complete the system by including radiation and its changing momentum is deemed to provide the force balance. But it may well suffice to recognize that the electromagnetic frame can be part of the whole system and may itself be able to assert force transiently to cater for the sporadic unbalance of force as two charges coexist in the general configuration of Fig. 5.

In developing (15) from (14) it was found that when two charges of identical mass move parallel there is strict balance of force and direct inverse-square law action between the charges. However, when the action is between charges of different mass, even parallel motion gives scope for out-of-balance force. One may then wonder what empirical evidence may exist in support of such dependence of the law of electrodynamics upon the mass ratio of the interacting charges.

The author has drawn attention to the early evidence of this from experiments on the anomalous cathode reaction forces associated with the vacuum arc (Aspden, 1969).* More recently there has been mounting evidence, as we shall see in discussion at the end of this work, that there are anomalous acceleration forces acting on ions in

* H. Aspden, *Journal of the Franklin Institute*, **287**, 179 (1969).

plasma. Suffice it here to mention that Sethian, Hammer and Wharton (1978)* have found:

> experimental evidence for an anomalous electron-ion energy transfer in a relativistic-electron-beam-heated plasma that is 10^3 times faster than can be predicted by classical processes.

At the end of the paper, the authors suggest 'without particular justification' that the anomalous factor might be the hydrogen ion to electron mass ratio, as applied in evaluating classical energy relaxation times in hydrogen. Thus the mass ratio M/m as used in the general law of electrodynamics (14) is in evidence as an anomalous acceleration of an ion by the action of electrons.

Clearly, such research, which is of great importance in fusion research where the object is to contain energy in the ions, can benefit from a solution of the unified field problem.

In proceeding, note that the word 'relativistic', as used in the above quotation, is intended to convey nothing other than that the electrons move at a high speed that is a significant fraction of the speed of light. There is no suggestion in the paper that the Theory of Relativity has any answers to offer in explaining the anomalies regularly reported in the electron-ion interaction.

It is of interest to examine what relativity does have to say on the subject of the electrodynamic law. Note that we arrived at the Lorentz Law of Force in (20). It applies to interaction involving a complete circuit, but it has been taken to apply as the corresponding Biot–Savart formulation to interaction between isolated pairs of charge in motion.

It was not until 1903 that an experiment was performed by Trouton and Noble† involving two parallel-moving charges, neither forming part of a closed circuit, but isolated on the plates of a charged capacitor. The mutual force was found to be directed along the line joining the charges and asserts no turning couple on the capacitor, as expected from (20). The motion was attributed to that of the Earth through space. The experiment is, therefore, not conclusive if one presumes that the Earth's electromagnetic reference frame moves along with it in its motion through space. It is inconclusive inasmuch

* J. D. Sethian, D. A. Hammer and C. B. Wharton, *Physical Review Letters*, **40**, 451 (1978).

† F. T. Trouton and R. H. Noble, *Proceedings of the Royal Society*, **72**, 132 (1903).

as an observer moving with the Earth will, by the relativistic argument, not sense any motion of charge on a capacitor moving with the observer. However, at the time of the experiment it could have been said to disprove the general application of the Lorentz law to charges in isolation. It did support the third law of electrodynamics presented by Maxwell, but appears not to have been considered in this context. Indeed, so far as the author is aware, the extra empirical fact provided by the Trouton–Noble experiment and needed to derive the empirical law of electrodynamics was not used for this purpose until the author examined its relevance (Aspden, 1969).*

Lorentz lost no time in reacting to the Trouton–Noble experiment because in 1904 he defended his law against the Trouton–Noble result by presenting his transformations and the contraction hypothesis.

The fact that the Lorentz law can be derived from Einstein's later theory is also no confirmation that it must be valid for action between isolated charge. The derivation in both cases depends upon the use of certain transformations with Maxwell's field equation:

$$\text{curl } V = -\frac{1}{c}\frac{dH}{dt} \tag{21}$$

Here V is the electric field intensity and H is the magnetic field intensity. t is time.

The equation was based upon an experimental observation involving the electromotive force in a closed wire loop. It was asserted that it applied equally to the total E.M.F. round any *closed* curve. As we then read from the text 'The Classical Theory of Electricity and Magnetism' by Abraham and Becker (1932):

> However, this . . . is in its complete generality a hypothesis, which we must justify by testing its consequences.

Its consequences have only been verified for actions involving closed circuits. The transformations in relativity implicitly introduced closed circuit conditions. Hence the Lorentz law of force cannot be relied upon in spite of its derivation from relativistic principles.

Inverse-Square Laws of Force

Much of accepted field theory is based upon the experimental foundation of Coulomb's Law and the observed propagation of

* See reference on p. 15.

electromagnetic waves. Maxwell's equations provide a well-tested starting point in field theory and are all the more secure because they have a linear form and are not affected by relativistic transformation. The fields represented can be superimposed and added vectorially. However, had the equations contained second-order terms, signifying energy density parameters, then the impact of relativity may well have been a different story.

In contrast, Coulomb's Law and Newton's Law of Gravitation both depend upon interactions which are second-order in this sense and both present difficulties when extended to relate to dynamic interactions.

Following the empirical example used in connection with the law of electrodynamics, we will study the interaction of bodies subject to an inverse-square of distance law of mutual force, but without adopting any field hypothesis. Our sole consideration will be the energy we associate with the interaction, taking energy as a scalar quantity and so avoiding the complications of the vector field.

The task is to derive a general formula $f(x, r)$ for the distribution $\partial E/\partial x$ denoting the element of energy ∂E distant x from a body A and contained within a spherical shell of thickness ∂x centred on that body. E is the energy associated with the interaction between body A and body B distant r from A. We know, since we are dealing with an inverse-square law of force, that the mutual force of attraction F is given by:

$$F = k/r^2 \qquad (22)$$

k is a constant which can be positive or negative for the Coulomb interaction, but which is invariably positive for the Newtonian gravitional interaction.

The force F can be expressed as a partial derivative of the energy E governing the interaction, with respect to the separation distance r, thus:

$$F = -\frac{\partial E}{\partial r} \qquad (23)$$

This also assures that action balances reaction, there being a mutua force of strength F asserted on A and B.

Introducing x, this becomes:

$$F = -\frac{\partial}{\partial r} \int_0^\infty \left(\frac{\partial E}{\partial x}\right) dx \qquad (24)$$

Our problem then is to determine the general solution for $f(x, r)$ which brings (24) into accord with (22).

The function $f(x, r)$ can be regarded as a function of x or r together with terms in x/r or terms in r/x. Then, bearing in mind that the energy under consideration is finite, given a finite value of r, we can expect $f(x, r)$ to be represented by a convergent power series in (x/r) when x is smaller than r or a convergent power series in (r/x) when x is larger than r. This follows from Maclaurin's Theorem. It may then be shown that the general solution must have the form:

$$f(x, r) = \frac{\partial E}{\partial x} = (1/r^2)\sum c_n(x/r)^n \qquad (25)$$

where the summation applies to all integral values of n. The coefficients c_n need to be determined, but to assure convergence they will be zero for n positive when x is large and for n negative when x is small.

With $n = 0$ or $n = -1$ we must have $c_n = 0$, because the integral in (24) would be otherwise be infinite.

Next, we observe that the function $f(x, r)$ can be restricted by the condition that it is invariable with r beyond a certain distance commensurate with r. This asserts that whatever the cause of the force interaction it is local to the immediate environment of the two interacting bodies. We are supposing that the energy E is located in the near vicinity of the bodies and that should some of this energy be remote its effect will be of little consequence to the interaction. In making this assertion one must depart from the idea embodied in the Mach Principle that remote stellar matter determines gravitational interaction locally. Our hypothesis is that force is connected solely with the interaction energy local to the two interacting bodies and we are guided to this hypothesis by the fact that the forces are not unduly retarded, as they would be if the energy had to migrate to and from remote areas.

Formulating this condition:

$$\frac{\partial}{\partial r}\left(\frac{\partial E}{\partial x}\right) = 0 \qquad (26)$$

for all x, when x is appreciably greater than r.

Restricting ourselves to this latter range, we combine (25) and (26) to obtain:

$$\frac{\partial}{\partial r}\left\{\frac{1}{r^2}\sum c_n(x/r)^n\right\} = -\frac{1}{r^3}\sum c_n(n+2)(x/r)^n = 0 \qquad (27)$$

Evidently n is -2 and all other c_n values applicable for the range where x is large must be zero.

This result is consistent with the argument that the applicable law of force must be dependent upon processes which somehow correlate with the symmetry of space. For example, a symmetrical emission from a point source has an intensity which diminishes as the square of distance from the source. Such an action suggests that only one term in n would apply in a general formulation such as (25), at least over the same range of x, as it seems unlikely that a multiplicity of physical actions could be involved in the same region of space, each action having a different symmetry connection and corresponding to a different term in n. Probably, therefore, the expression $f(x, r)$ will contain but a single $(x/r)^n$ term over a given range of x, as we have just found where x is large in relation to r.

Since we are considering the distribution of energy in space it is helpful at this stage to examine two possibilities. Firstly, case (a) for which the interaction energy tends to be as close as possible to either body as reference and, secondly, case (b) for which the interaction energy tends to be as remote as possible from either body as reference. This is of interest because there are two basic inverse-square laws, Newton's Law of Gravitation and Coulomb's Law and there is a physical difference which poses questions. With gravitation like bodies mutually attract and with the electrostatic interaction like bodies mutually repel. The energy transfer processes could then be different in the two cases, one finding its energy from a primary source which tends to minimize and so forces a higher concentration of local energy in the reaction process and the other being, in fact, a process involving the primary energy which seeks to feed a reaction and so diminishes locally.

The solution for the case (a) interaction has a unique form if we specify that it must be the most simple solution having a single transition in the form of $(x/r)^n$ at the distance $x = r$ determined by the physical spacing of the two bodies. For x greater than r we have found that $n = -2$. For x less than r the tendency of E to be as close to the reference body A as possible means that n must be as low as possible. We also know that the convergence requirement means that n is a positive integer over this range. Hence $n = 1$. The resulting spatial energy distribution for case (a) is shown in Fig. 12, drawn to avoid an energy discontinuity at $x = r$.

As will be shown, there are reasons for identifying this particular energy distribution with the gravitational interaction.

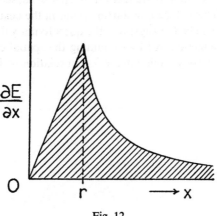

Fig. 12

The solution for case (b) requires the interaction energy to be as remote from the reference body as possible. This is the case for the unique solution that there is no energy at all over the range of x from O to r. The interaction energy is all confined to the space beyond $x = r$, where the $(x/r)^{-2}$ term applies. The resulting energy distribution is shown in Fig. 13.

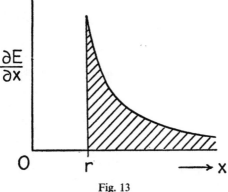

Fig. 13

Note that we are considering energy summed within concentric shells of space centred on either A or B as reference body and not interaction energy *densities*. These do have finite positive or negative values within the range from $x = 0$ to $x = r$.

The particular energy distribution of Fig. 13 may be readily identified with Coulomb interaction by analysis based upon classical field theory. This will be our starting point in the next chapter. Also, our objective will be to progress in the quest to unify the gravitational and electromagnetic force by examining the spatial energy distribution of the electrodynamic interaction in relation to Fig. 12.

2

Gravitation and Magnetism

Retardation

The Coulomb interaction is fundamental in physics. In terms of electric field theory the energy density throughout space surrounding two interacting electric charges at rest can readily be calculated. When summed throughout space the resulting energy is found to depend upon the separation of the two charges and its dependence upon this spacing allows us to verify the Coulomb law of force.

The distribution of this energy becomes very important when we investigate the effects of charge motion upon energy deployment and the resulting interaction force.

Given two charges e and e' at a separation distance r, the charges now being in electrostatic units, we find that there is a Coulomb interaction energy ee'/r stored in the surrounding space, together with the energy of self-interaction of each charge, the latter being related to e^2 and $(e')^2$, respectively. The self-energy is that representing the mass of each charge. We expect then that as the two charges separate, assuming that they have like polarity, the interaction energy diminishes and is shared by the two charges in augmenting their self-energies. In other words they gain kinetic energy which augments their mass energy.

The question of interest is the mechanism of energy transfer from the surrounding space to the close proximity of either charge. This question led the author to ask about the spatial distribution of the interaction energy as viewed from either charge. Hence the interest in the previous chapter in working out the energy content of successive concentric shells centred on each charge and plotting this as a function of distance from the charge.

It is fascinating to find that the interaction energy, as seen from the perspective of either charge, is seated beyond the charge separation distance r. This was evident from Fig. 13, but we will now verify this using conventional field theory. Note first, however, that energy has to traverse the distance separating the charges in order to converge on the close locality of a receiving charge to augment its kinetic energy, particularly if one charge is relatively slow moving owing to its greater mass. The latter condition is one in which most of the interaction energy released is fed to speed up the lighter charge.

There is a quite simple graphical way of deriving the energy distribution shown in Fig. 13.* Consider a charge e in Fig. 14 developing a radial electric field V at radius x. Imagine then a charge e' distant r from e and developing an electric field V', at the radius x.

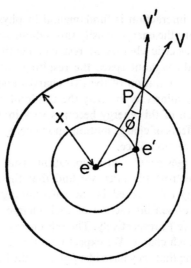

Fig. 14

Let y denote the distance between e' and a point P under consideration at radius x from e. Then, with φ as the angle between V and V', we know that the interaction energy density component at P is:

$$\frac{VV'\cos\varphi}{4\pi} \tag{28}$$

Also, V is e/x^2 and V' is e'/y^2. Now consider the volume of an elemental shell of the sphere of radius x and thickness dx, as subtended at P by a small solid angle from e'. The elemental volume is $y^2/\cos\varphi$ times this angle per unit thickness of the shell. Thus the

* H. Aspden, *Lett. Nuovo Cimento*, **25**, 456 (1979).

energy attributable to (28) in a shell of thickness dx is $ee'dx/4\pi x^2$ times the solid angle mentioned. Since this does not depend upon y, we can evaluate the total energy component dE for the full solid angle of 4π to obtain:

$$dE = ee'dx/x^2 \qquad (29)$$

Now, provided x is greater than r, the fields V and V' are in the same direction. With x less than r the two regions of the spherical shell intercepted by the same solid angle have opposite and cancelling interaction energies owing to the change in direction of V relative to V'. Thus within the radius r the interaction field energy is zero.

This fully confirms the result inferred by a general interpretation of the inverse-square law of force, leading to the spatial energy distribution shown in Fig. 13.

If e and e' are in motion at the same velocity and carry their intrinsic electric fields bodily with them there will be no energy transfer and no retardation affecting the Coulomb force. Thus retardation of the electric action is not an answer to the electrodynamic interaction. The law of electrodynamics presented in Chapter 1 is attributable to magnetic effects, which, as we shall presently see, arise from the reaction of the space medium. However, if e and e' have velocities which differ, then there will be retardation associated with the electric interaction. Since electric fields propagate at the speed c, where c is the familiar parameter used in the mass-energy relationship $E = Mc^2$, we know, from Fig. 13, that it takes a time r/c for an acceleration pulse at e to communicate its effect to the interaction energy in the field. It takes exactly the same time r/c for e' to communicate with the interaction energy in the field. Accordingly, the total retardation time is $2r/c$ for the Coulomb interaction. Energy takes this time to transfer via the field from e to e' and energy in transit may not assert its action as part of the interaction energy accounting for the Coulomb force.

If the action of one electric charge on another is propagated a distance r in time $2r/c$ then the speed of propagation of disturbances in a sea of electric charge is $\frac{1}{2}c$. This is not to be confused with the propagation of electromagnetic waves or electric field disturbance. It is the displacement speed of charge in the propagation direction. This result will be applied later in this chapter.

Let us now consider the alternative spatial energy distribution presented in Fig. 12. This is presented again in Fig. 15, which includes

an additional cross-shaded triangle to indicate the change resulting if
r is reduced slightly. If *r* is reduced the interaction energy changes by
the amount corresponding to the area of this triangle. Energy does
not have to travel the full distance *r*, on average, to reach the interaction field. When there is a change in the spacing *r* between the

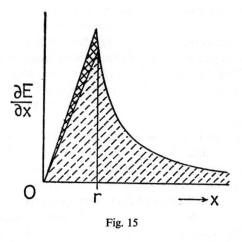

Fig. 15

interacting bodies the energy has to travel a distance $\frac{2}{3}r$ on average.
This is because an energy element proportional to *x* travels a distance
x and we need to evaluate the integral of the product of the two over
the range O to *r* and find the average distance by dividing by the
integral of the energy element factor *x* over the same range.

However, when considering the effects as a retardation we find
that a retardation effect on energy has a perturbing action on force in
proportion to the retardation squared. Therefore, in working out a
mean retardation time for the above action, we must evaluate a root
mean square of the elemental components of this time. So we need to
know the root mean square of the distance travelled by the energy.
This is the square root of the integral of $x^3 dx$ divided by the square
root of the integral of $x dx$ over the range O to *r*. The effective distance
is $r/\sqrt{2}$.

The retardation time *T* is then the time taken to travel this distance
to the field at the speed *c* and the time to make a similar return
journey between the field and the other body. We may write:

$$T^2 = 2(r/c)^2 \tag{30}$$

This retardation effect is one half that applicable for the spatial energy distribution corresponding to the Coulomb Law.

The Law of Gravitation

The most direct way in which to assess the effects of such a retardation for the interaction between sun and planet is to calculate the associated gravitational energy deficit, that is the amount in transit and so ineffective in asserting force on the planet.

The centrifugal acceleration f of the planet is v^2/r, where v is the orbital velocity in a circular orbit of radius r. This acceleration acting for the retardation period T gives a measure of the displacement under the central gravitational force corresponding to the deficit energy quantity:

$$\left(\frac{GMm}{r^2}\right)(\tfrac{1}{2}fT^2) \tag{31}$$

Here G is the constant of gravitation, M is the mass of the sun and m is the mass of the planet. M has been taken to be so much greater than m that the separation distance r is effectively the same as the radius of the planetary orbit. Newton's Law of Gravitation has been used in obtaining this result. Now put f as v^2/r and substitute T from (30). The energy deficit given by (31) becomes:

$$\left(\frac{GMm}{r}\right)(v/c)^2 \tag{32}$$

The quantity $-GMm/r$ is the gravitational potential energy of the system. Therefore, the effect of retardation, if we assume that gravitation involves a law of force conforming with the case (a) situation leading to the spatial energy distribution in Fig. 12, is to increase G as it applies in Newton's Law of Gravitation, effectively by the factor:

$$1 + (v/c)^2 \tag{33}$$

In terms of force, note that conservation of angular momentum renders v inversely proportional to r, making the v-dependent *energy* term inversely proportional to r^3. This means that, upon differentiation with respect to r to obtain a force expression, the factor (33) converts to:

$$1 + 3(v/c)^2 \tag{34}$$

Thus, in a force equation, the value of G needs to be increased by this factor in order to account for retardation effects. This modifies Newton's Law of Gravitation:

$$\frac{d^2u}{d\varphi} + u = GM/h^2 \tag{35}$$

to:
$$\frac{d^2u}{d\varphi} + u = GM/h^2 + 3GM(u^2/c^2) \tag{36}$$

These are laws of motion based on the force relationship and expressed in polar coordinates u, φ. u is $1/r$ and $h = vr$.

Equation (36) is the law of gravitation which emerges from Einstein's General Theory of Relativity.

Had we used the spatial distribution of Fig. 13, as applies to Coulomb's Law, we would have obtained double the last term in (36). Hence, we can take this derivation based on the Fig. 12 distribution as correctly applicable to the problem of gravitation.

We are now a step further along in our quest to unify the electro-dynamic and the gravitational force relationships. We have bridged the link between the basic inverse-square law and the law obtained from General Relativity.

It is of interest to pause here to discuss some aspects of this law of gravitation. Newton's Law is often said to be incorrect, when in fact it is a valid law for action at a distance. If gravitation is propagated at a finite speed then retardation has to be considered. This was well appreciated in the nineteenth century. Planets describe elliptical orbits. They continuously exchange kinetic energy with the gravitational potential of the sun-and-planet interaction. If the energy has to travel across distances of the order of the orbital radius of a planet then retardation effects can become important. The radial perturbation is subject to retardation which causes the natural frequency of oscillation radially to be less than the orbital frequency. As a result, the major axis of the elliptical orbit will advance progressively, producing an anomalous motion of perihelion.

The advance of Mercury's perihelion was, therefore, attributed to retardation. Gerber (1898)* presented an analysis and formulated the relationship between Mercury's perihelion motion and the speed of propagation of gravitation. His paper was entitled: 'The Space and Time Propagation of Gravitation'. His formula was exactly that later

* P. Gerber, *Zeitschrift f. Math. u. Phys.*, **43**, 93 (1898).

presented by Einstein, in applying his General Theory of Relativity to the same problem. The object of the paper was to show that gravitation is propagated at exactly the speed of light. It was following the publication on Einstein's Theory in 1916 that a paper (Gerber, 1917) repeating and expanding Gerber's analysis was submitted to *Annalen der Physik*, the journal publishing Einstein's paper. It issued in January, 1917. Seelinger immediately drew attention to a mathematical flaw in the Gerber analysis. Oppenheim responded, stressing that the issue of finite speed was still open, but Seelinger reasserted his position to ensure that his arguments were not eroded by Oppenheim's views.*

Such was the climate, but it was difficult to imagine that energy transferred between sun and planet at other than the speed of light and, when applied to transit along the path between sun and planet, it gives the wrong answer.

As recently as 1970, Brillouin† has reminded us that the question of the finite speed of gravitation is still open. Brillouin also refers to and endorses Heaviside's 1893 advice to study the spatial distribution of the interaction energy. The author has followed this advice and found that Einstein's equation for gravitation does result, simply because the energy travels from sun to planet via an indirect route. It goes into the field regions of surrounding space on its way. The energy travels at the speed of light along this route but it takes a little longer to reach the planet than do the direct rays from the sun.

The question now remains as to how gravitation can be correlated with electromagnetism. We need to establish that the electrodynamic interaction discussed in Chapter 1 has a spatial energy distribution conforming with Fig. 12. This will complete the unification as to form, because the direct inverse-square of attraction law has been found to be a specific case of the general law of electrodynamics of equation (14) and we have just seen how to develop a law of motion according to Einstein's General Theory, given one of the Newton form.

It is not possible to work out the magnetic field energy density in the space surrounding two interacting charges and, by integration, derive formulae for the spatial energy distribution. The reason is that the usual magnetic field formula is a derivation from the Lorentz Law

---

* See *Ann. d. Phys.*, **52**, 415 (1917), **53**, 31 and 163 (1917), **54**, 38 (1917).
† L. Brillouin, *Relativity Reexamined*, Academic Press, New York, 1970.

of Force (20). It is only valid for applications involving closed cir-cuital currents. Hence the results of integrating magnetic field energy based on this formula are unreliable. The calculations have, however, been made and the spatial energy distributions plotted (Eagles and Aspden, 1980),* but, as Moon and Spencer (1954)† have argued, the Lorentz law as applied to isolated charges:

> is untenable and the whole process of defining a magnetic field from this equation is unsound.

The magnetic field concept seems only to have meaning in its present formulation if applied strictly to the closed circuit interaction. Therefore, we have a problem of knowing how to proceed to discover the electrodynamic spatial energy distribution.

Electromagnetism

The nature of the magnetic field is one of the most perplexing problems in physics. Magnetic energy appears for some purposes to have a negative potential, as evidenced by the mutual attraction of two parallel conductors carrying currents in the same direction. This is analogous in some respects with the action of gravitation, also a phenomenon represented by a negative potential. Yet, in other respects, as in the case of the magnetic energy stored in an induction coil, there is every sign that the energy seeks to transform into another energy form as if it has potential energy which tends to reduce. To understand this phenomenon it does not suffice to rely on empirical formulation. Some deeper insight into the energy transfer processes seems essential.

We will approach the problem from first principles and regard the existence of charge and electric field energy as basic. The motion of such charge through the space medium gives rise to magnetic effects. Our only scope, then, for probing this medium is to be guided by the fact that it can sustain Maxwell's displacement currents and assert that this space medium itself contains electric charge in an overall neutral state. To proceed in the most plausible way we will use the hypothesis that space is permeated by a uniform electric continuum of charge density σ and that within this continuum there are numer-ous identical charges q of opposite polarity. Here q is an electrostatic

* D. M. Eagles and H. Aspden, *Acta Physica Polonica*, A57 (1980).
  † P. Moon and D. E. Spencer, *Journal of the Franklin Institute*, 257, 305 (1954).

charge. This is a working hypothesis not invented to explain the propagation of light, as was the classical aether, but rather to provide us with a starting point and a reference frame for motion, as well as a system whose energy characteristics can be formulated.

Initially we will consider the electrostatics of such a system. The charges q will be termed 'lattice particles' because they will form themselves into some kind of lattice arrangement. Indeed, they will define a structure in the space medium. Imagine that the effects of a disturbing charge e, not itself part of the space medium, cause the lattice particles to be displaced to new positions of equilibrium. Thus at a given region of the medium all the lattice particles will be displaced a distance D in company with one another. Whatever the direction of this displacement each particle will move from O on one side of a planar slice of the continuum to P on the other side of this planar slice. OP is the distance D. This is depicted in Fig. 16.

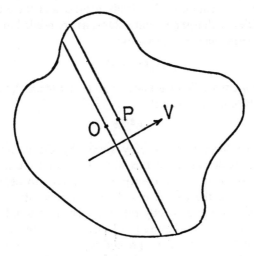

Fig. 16

The particle displacement will be a collective displacement corresponding to the presence of an electric field of intensity V, taken to be uniform over the section of the space medium depicted in Fig. 16. Thus there will be no change in the Coulomb force on any particle due to the action of its neighbours. They move in register with one another locally and remote actions balance anyway owing to the large scale distortions of the lattice structure governed by the charge e and boundary conditions. Any restoring force on the lattice particles will be that due to the planar slice of continuum of thickness D.

By Gauss' Theorem a planar slice of charge density σ and thickness D has a total normal electric field intensity of $4\pi\sigma D$ of which half is directed one way and the other half the opposite way. Hence $4\pi\sigma D$ is the change in field intensity experienced by a lattice particle in going from O to P owing to the action of the field V. The restoring force on q is therefore:

$$4\pi q D \qquad (37)$$

This is equal to Vq. The energy stored by this displacement per charge q is:

$$\tfrac{1}{2}(4\pi\sigma q)D^2 \qquad (38)$$

because the restoring force rate is linear with displacement. The energy density represented by (38) is found by multiplying by σ/q since the space medium is electrically neutral and there are just as many particles of charge q in unit volume as are needed to balance σ. Thus the energy density is given by:

$$\tfrac{1}{2}(4\pi\sigma^2)D^2 \qquad (39)$$

But since Vq equals (37) we know that D is $V/4\pi\sigma$. Putting this in (39) gives the energy density:

$$V^2/8\pi \qquad (40)$$

This is the formula for energy stored by the electric field of intensity V. Its derivation in this way means that the hypothetical system proposed has the property of being able to deploy energy from the field of the charge e and transfer this into electric field energy associated more directly with the space medium. Put another way, the electric field of the charge e has, at least in the main body of the space medium where there are charges q, been cancelled by displacement of this electrical medium. Here then is the basis for the displacement currents we associate with Maxwell's theory.

Examine now the disturbance caused by a charge e moving along a line CB at velocity v, as shown in Fig. 17. We study the effect upon a charge q displaced from its neutral position at A when e is at B. BA is a separation vector r making an angle θ with v. The position of q will change according to the velocity v. q is at A_1 for $v=0$, but moves to A_2 when e has a finite velocity. Note that A_1 and A_2 are in the very near vicinity of A and are effectively at A for the purpose of evaluating the electric field acting directly from e at B. For e at rest at B, A_1 is on the extension of BA. For e in motion, the effect of e is seen at A to emanate from a previous position of e, the position C. Thus A_2 lies on CA extended. A_1A_2 is drawn normal to CA because it represents an electric field vector not compensated by displacement. Energy

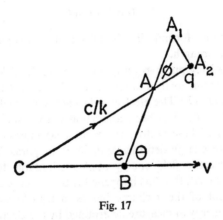

Fig. 17

minimization requires a minimization of this vector, making the angle between AA_2 and A_1A_2 a right angle.

The position of C can be determined, provided we know the speed at which the disturbance of the q charges propagates. Earlier in this chapter, just before we introduced Fig. 15, it was shown that this speed is $\frac{1}{2}c$. Readers may, however, not feel too comfortable about accepting this, because the concept of a natural propagation in the vacuum medium at half the speed of light is unfamiliar. Therefore, we will proceed using a general propagation speed c/k, where k is a constant believed by the author to be 2, on the basis of earlier analysis in this work.

The position of C is then seen to be given by the relationship:

$$CB/CA = kv/c \qquad (41)$$

Let φ denote the angle between BA and CA. Since displacement is linearly proportional to electric field intensity we can then see that, if A_1A_2 represents a field of strength V, V becomes $\sin\varphi$ times the field intensity of e at A. Thus:

$$V = (e/r^2)\sin\varphi \qquad (42)$$

By the sine formula:

$$CB\sin\theta = CA\sin\varphi \tag{43}$$

From (41) this is:

$$\sin\varphi = (kv/c)\sin\theta \tag{44}$$

Therefore, from (42) and (44):

$$V = (kev/r^2c)\sin\theta \tag{45}$$

which is Ampère's formula if k is unity and V is considered as the magnetic field strength.

Let us tentatively put k as unity and explore the field represented by V with electromagnetism in mind. How is the electric field energy deployed in Fig. 17? The electric field energy normally associated with the vector AA_1 has been apportioned to sustain the vectors AA_2 and A_2A_1. These vectors represent field intensities. They are squared to give energy densities and, by Pythagoras' Theorem, we see that the electric field energy at A attributable to the charge motion v is zero. All that has happened is that electric energy stored by displacement of the q charge has been transformed into non-displacement energy in measure determined by the electric field given by (45).

Accordingly, even if we speak of V as a magnetic field, we cannot, without further justification, state that there is a magnetic field energy added by motion of e at velocity v.

To resolve this problem let us simply be mindful of the fact that our experience of magnetic fields comes from collective motion of charge and not isolated charge in motion. It is likely to be the combined effect of numerous charges in motion that really cause the displacements of the q charges and the overall action may be quite complex. Indeed, the effect at A in Fig. 17 may well be moderated by inducing a reaction in the motion of other charge. A primary electric field disturbance at A, caused by the motion of charge e, represents a non-equilibrium state and is conducive to actions which tend to restore equilibrium. Therefore we can contemplate the electric displacement as a catalyst by which optimum reaction conditions prevail in the dynamic state. This is the process of induction, involving the transfer of energy from the primary charge to a reacting charge. This so-called magnetic energy is shared by reacting charge distributed throughout the space surrounding the charge e and takes the form of kinetic energy of the other charges in reacting motion.

The field parameter given by (45) is a measure of the field disturbance associated with this inductive process, but it does not tell us how much energy is transferred to the reacting system. To discover this, we argue that the electromagnetic disturbance is, in field terms, proportional to ev. In energy terms, the electromagnetic disturbance will be proportional to the sum of the cross products of the ev parameters for all the interacting primary charges. This follows from dimensional considerations, but formulation is no easy task because it depends upon the spacing and directions of the several interacting primary charges. Note also that we are not just concerned with the total magnetic field energy involved in the electrodynamic interaction. This could be deduced from the force relationships examined in Chapter 1. Our object is to determine the spatial energy distribution of this energy so that we can examine the retardation issue.

The optimum reaction conditions will undoubtedly require a maximization of the energy drawn from the electrodynamic retardation of two primary interacting charges in motion. Only the settled equilibrium state will be in evidence in our physical observations. Thus, when two primary charges of like polarity move in parallel at a controlled and set speed, their concerted action to maximize the reaction energy will urge them together, giving rise to the electrodynamic interaction force. More generally, we know from the analysis in Chapter 1 leading to equations (9) and (10) that the electrodynamic interaction between charges, however directed, incorporates, as its controlling component, a direct inverse-square law of force, which we can now attribute to the magnetic energy stored in the reacting system.

This permits us to regard the magnetic energy as distributed spatially according either to case (a) or case (b), as discussed at the end of Chapter 1. We spoke there of the distinction between these cases, regarding case (a), the Fig. 12 distribution, as that for which the interaction energy tended to be as close to the interacting bodies as possible, with case (b), the Fig. 13 distribution, being that for which the interaction energy tended to be as remote as possible from either body. However, Nature may not so distinguish in establishing the dual existence of such energy distributions. It could well be that there are constraints provided by a true electric field action and the case (b) distribution for the Coulomb energy may arise from field behaviour, as analysed early in this chapter. Then, so far as case (a) is concerned, this distribution may rather be the only natural distribution governed by the self-distribution of energy. We know that thermal energy does not seek to escape from its source. Rather, it seeks to distribute itself in a uniform manner, filling the space available with thermal energy at a uniform temperature. Then, so far as case (a) energy distribution is concerned, we can imagine that this is a condition of maximum energy dispersal within the constraints applied. The constraint is that $n = -2$ when x is greater than r, as we saw from equation (27). Maximum dispersal means minimum ordinate for the energy term $\partial E/\partial x$ at r. Thus as much energy as possible must lie between O and r. Yet n has to be a positive integer over this range. Accordingly, it must be unity, giving the case (a) situation already discussed.

Dispersal of energy is a characteristic of the thermal or dynamic state and it is natural to associate this with magnetic energy. However, whereas thermal energy in the experience we have from dissociation processes tends to fill the space available in a uniform way linked to the uniformity of the substance present, magnetic energy is constrained by the presence of the primary charge influence upon electric displacement in the vacuum medium. The magnetic reaction energy is dispersed in a manner which assures that the overall reaction is in balance with the primary action.

The Gyromagnetic Reaction

From the above argument, we see that the analysis leading to equation (45) tells us very little about magnetic action. It suggests that the electrodynamic disturbance could be larger by the factor k, double that expected classically, if the analysis is to be given credence, but we have had to infer, rather than deduce by formulation, the spatial energy distribution which is to be associated with the magnetic reaction.

Be this as it may, the task ahead is one of verification. If the argument is correct, the magnetic field energy is really stored as the kinetic energy of reacting charge and we can, presumably, consider as reacting the electrons in matter or the q charges in the vacuum, inasmuch as both can have motion components superimposed upon other ordered motion. However, the reaction must itself be somehow ordered from the magnetic viewpoint if it is to moderate the effects of primary charge in causing the displacement portrayed in Fig. 17.

The reaction develops reaction currents, which can become primary and transfer their energies back to the source circuits, in a circuit configuration.

The need to recognize this reaction phenomenon may have eluded physicists because there is no apparent evidence of free electron diamagnetism when magnetic fields are applied to electrical conductors. If there are free electrons moving around in conductors, as we believe, how is it that in a steady magnetic field they do not develop a reacting helical motion and substantially cancel the field? This is a classical problem. There was no evidence of substantial diamagnetism, and so statistical arguments were applied and, unfortunately, these are based on some rather arbitrary assumptions. The subject is well summarized in a book by Van Vleck (1932).* Statistics were applied in a way which tends to conflict with the accepted laws of magnetic induction. Reactions which require angular momentum of electrons to be unidirectional were avoided by asserting that angular momentum is shared equally between opposite directions. Alternatively, it is argued that there are collisions between electrons and the notional boundaries of a conductor and these collisions supposedly introduce a reverse component of angular momentum. Another argument is that the Lorentz force on a reacting charge is at right angles to the charge motion. Hence the magnetic field to which the charge is reacting cannot transfer energy to the reacting charge, which in turn means that there is no diamagnetism. All these arguments are unconvincing. They require arbitrary and questionable assumptions, especially the latter, which seems to deny Faraday's discovery of induction. It is better to accept that diamagnetism exists and investigate why its effects are hidden.†

First, note that if there is no externally applied magnetic field the random motion of free charge in a conductor will not become a concerted motion producing fields of its own accord. Each charge in motion is potentially both a primary field producer and potentially a reacting charge developing a field in opposition. There are statistical exchanges of role which assure that there is no overall polarization of the magnetic action. However, if we apply a magnetic

* J. H. Van Vleck, *The Theory of Electric and Magnetic Susceptibilities*, Oxford University Press, 1932.

† This problem was the starting point of the whole research recorded in this book, which began in 1955 shortly after the author completed his Ph.D. research at Trinity College, Cambridge, on more orthodox aspects of magnetic reaction effects.

field, then there must be some reaction producing diamagnetism. But not all the charges in motion in the conductor participate at the same time. They will, as before, tend to oppose the field actions of one another, but will, in some optimum way, react to the applied field to a limited extent.

Thus, we take the true applied field to be H_o and suppose this to be offset by a diamagnetic reaction field H_r to produce an effective field H. Thus:

$$H_o - H_r = H \qquad (46)$$

By Lorentz's law the force Hev/c acts on a charge e of mass m moving at speed v perpendicular to the magnetic field of strength H. Then the charge is deflected into a circular orbit with this force in balance with centrifugal action:

$$Hev/c = mv^2/x \qquad (47)$$

x is the radius of the orbit. Regardless of the direction of motion or the polarity of the charge, the deflection is always in the sense that results in a reaction field. This is found from the reaction current moment $evx/2c$, that is the area πx^2 times the current $ev/2\pi xc$.

Thus the total reaction current moment per unit volume of the field is given by:

$$\sum(evx/2c) = \sum(\tfrac{1}{2}mv^2)/H \qquad (48)$$

from (47). The summations apply to unit volume. The value of H_r is, conventionally, 4π times this quantity, but we will now introduce the factor k of (45), because the theory developed tells us that k should not be ignored. Thus:

$$H_r = 4\pi k E/H \qquad (49)$$

where E now replaces the kinetic energy density of the reaction.

Combining (46) and (49) we obtain:

$$H_o H - 4\pi k E = H^2 \qquad (50)$$

k is constant and, as we have seen, the magnetic interaction requires energy to be fed to the kinetic energy of the reacting system to the maximum extent possible. Hence there will be diamagnetism set by the condition that E is a maximum in (50). H will vary as a result to assure that:

$$H_o = 2H \qquad (51)$$

It follows that the field is invariably halved by diamagnetism of free charge. For this to pass undetected in our research the magnetic field theory must account for a doubling of the magnetic effects of charge in motion. Thus the factor k in (45) must be 2, and it is interesting to find that we had already anticipated this from the analysis of retardation in Coulomb interaction. It is thus explained why this diamagnetic aspect of all magnetic field reactions had eluded detection.

The value of the kinetic energy density E can also be determined from (50) and (51). With $k=2$, E is found to be $H^2/8\pi$. This is the magnetic field energy density formula. It confirms that the reaction component of kinetic energy density can be identified as magnetic field energy, as already suggested.

We are led to the result that the establishment of a magnetic field, whether in materials or the vacuum, leads to the injection of kinetic energy of amount we associate with magnetic field energy. This energy will merge with the thermal energy but at least this amount of kinetic energy must always be present to sustain the reaction. Even the vacuum cannot 'cool' below the temperature needed to sustain this magnetic field. We will come back to this in Chapter 9 when it will be shown how this accounts for the cosmic background radiation temperature in the vicinity of the Earth.

Next, before returning to the problem of unifying electrodynamic and gravitational force, we will digress just a little to observe that the factor $k=2$ is very much in evidence in an experiment dating from 1923.

Richardson (1908) suggested that when the magnetism in a pivotally mounted ferromagnetic rod is reversed, the rod should experience a counter-balancing change of angular momentum.* It was expected that the gyromagnetic ratio, the ratio of the change of angular momentum to the change of magnetic moment, should be $2mc/e$. This was the quantity applicable to the electron in free orbital motion, where e is the electron charge, m its mass and c the speed of light in vacuo. Einstein and Haas (1915)† first observed the effect. Sucksmith and Bates (1923) then found that the effect was only one half of that predicted.‡

This halving effect is, of course, in full accord with the magnetic moment being double that expected on conventional theory. The

---

* O. W. Richardson, *Physical Review*, **26**, 248 (1908).
† A. Einstein and W. J. Haas, *Verh. d. Deutsch. Phys. Ges.*, **17**, 152 (1915).
‡ W. Sucksmith and L. F. Bates, *Proc. Roy. Soc. London*, **104A**, 499 (1923).

reacting conduction electrons halve the magnetic moment, but they also halve the angular momentum of the overall electron contribution. Therefore, the experiment gives a true measure of the gyromagnetic ratio and confirms that $k = 2$.

The gyromagnetic ratio has been related to the half-spin quantum of electrons and caused physicists to regard the ferromagnetic state as due to electron spin, rather than orbital motion. Theoretically, the factor of 2 features in the quantum-based relativistic treatment of Dirac, but this is a little abstract in character and so can be questioned, especially in the light of the alternative account in this work. A slight departure from the factor of 2 is observed in measurements of the spin magnetic moment of the electron. Indeed, the anomalous g-factor, as this is called, is regarded as one of the theoretical triumphs of quantum electrodynamics. We will come back to this in Chapter 5. Meanwhile, we revert to the problem of gravitation.

The Graviton

We set out to discover the spatial energy distribution associated with the electrodynamic interaction. Magnetic field theory was avoided because in its conventional form it applies only to closed circuit interactions. By inference from the fact that magnetic field energy is a kinetic energy of environmental charge in a reacting mode, we have found that the spatial energy distribution is of the form needed to establish the link with gravitation.

Hence we can, with confidence, embark upon the task of determining how the Neumann Potential given by equation (8) can become a gravitational potential.

The answer lies in the recognition that there exist in the continuum of the vacuum medium what will be termed 'gravitons'. These are very small in physical size and they adjust in size to store energy and so complement and balance the mass-energy of matter present. This adjustment affects their electrodynamic action, bearing in mind that they displace the charge in the continuum. Then, their concerted mutually-parallel motion relative to the electrodynamic reference frame set by the q charge system induces a small electrodynamic effect, which causes an inverse-square force of mutual attraction, an electrodynamic action, which we will identify as the gravitational interaction. The Constant of Gravitation G will be deduced in terms of the mass-energy of the graviton and the latter will be verified both by theoretical enquiry and experimental evidence linked to elementary particle physics.

It is in this way that we will establish the connection between the gravitational and electromagnetic action, the study of the spatial energy distribution associated with these phenomena having shown us that Einstein's formula for gravitation does have common ground with electrodynamics. However, we have to pursue this enquiry against the background of success of Einstein's General Theory of Relativity and it is appropriate to comment briefly on the broader gravitational questions posed by this theory.

There are essentially three tests of Einstein's General Theory of Relativity. These are the planetary perihelion advance, the effects of gravitation upon light speed and deflection and, finally, the gravitational red shift. The first two of these tests relate to the equation of motion associated with Einstein's law of gravitation. These, therefore, support, with equal effect, the retardation thesis on which the same law has been derived in this work. The third test, the red shift, has never been regarded as a particularly strong test of general relativity. The red shift is hardly more than Nature's recognition that the emission of spectral lines by atoms depends upon energy states which, in turn, depend upon gravitational action. Dicke (1964) in his book *The Theoretical Significance of Experimental Relativity* dismisses the red shift with the words:

> The red shift can be obtained from the null result of the Eotvos experiment, mass-energy equivalence, and the conservation of energy in a static gravitational field and static co-ordinate system. For this reason the gravitational red shift is not a very strong test of general relativity.

In Dicke's book just mentioned he also writes:

> To me the geometry of a physical space is primarily a subjective concept. What is objective is the material content of space, the photons, electrons, pions, neutrinos, protons etc., and *gravitons*. I give emphasis to the idea, not yet substantiated by observations, that in the same sense that electromagnetic forces are induced by interactions with photons, gravitational forces are due to collisions with gravitons. I here use the word 'graviton' in a generic sense to mean any type of particle responsible for the effect of gravitation.

The idea that gravitational effects are due to collisions with gravitons presents great difficulties, if one relies too heavily on the analogy with photons. The author prefers to retain the electrodynamic interaction concept as the basis for explaining gravitation and look to the mediating action of the graviton in the process. Already, the electrodynamic approach has shown how we can develop a link with the form of the Einstein law of gravitation. The General Theory of Relativity is no obstacle either to this approach. To progress towards a successful theory of gravitation we need to derive the Constant of Gravitation G in terms of other fundamental quantities, as, for example, the graviton energy quantum, and then demonstrate that this energy quantum exists in Nature. We, therefore, are set on a course which causes us to challenge some of the fundamentals of Einstein's theories, as we enquire into the elementary particle world revealed by the inherent properties of the vacuum medium.

At the beginning of this chapter we examined the nature of the space medium permeating the vacuum. It is electrically neutral but is full of charges q set in a sea of opposite charge of uniform charge density σ. We have found that the correct law of electrodynamics applicable to action between discrete electric charges gives a direct inverse-square attraction force provided the charges are like charges moving mutually parallel. The mutual gravitational force between two electrons is 10^{-39} times that of their Coulomb repulsion. The mutual electrodynamic attraction between two electrons, according to the law derived, is $(v/c)^2$ times their Coulomb repulsion, where v is their common velocity and c is the speed of light. Thus, the electrons would have to move extremely slowly to experience an electrodynamic interaction matching their gravitational interaction. Accordingly, we should not look to the charge possessed by matter when seeking to understand gravitation, especially as gravitation is a property of matter which is electrically neutral overall.

We are left, therefore, to examine the effect of the charge continuum σ. Imagine that matter and the structured lattice formed by the q charges define our local electromagnetic frame of reference and regard σ as having a universal flow (which could be oscillatory). Consider what happens as this uniformly-dense continuum of charge is deflected past an electron. This is pictured in Fig. 18. The electron is depicted as a sphere obstructing the flow. The uniformly-dense character of the continuum charge makes this situation analogous to that of the flow of an incompressible fluid through a pipe in which there is an obstruction partially impeding the flow. The amount of fluid flowing through the pipe is unaffected. It is just that the fluid speeds up in passing the obstruction. Thus, the electrodynamic effect of the flow of continuum charge is unaffected by the presence of the electron. The continuum has merely gone a little faster in being

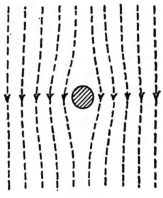

Fig. 18

diverted around the electron. This, therefore, gives us no scope for developing a small electrodyamic effect associated with the existence of the electron.

But remember that we need to relate the effect with mass and that 'gravitons' have been mentioned. Assume that gravitons are standard-sized spheres possessing the same charge e as normal elementary particles, but differing in the one respect that they move with the continuum. It may then appear that this is of no help either in attacking our problem of relating electrodynamic action with the mass of matter, because the mass of the electron in Fig. 18 plays no role and the electrodynamic effects are in no way connected with the electron.

There is, however, one fundamental difference between the effect of the electron and that of the graviton. The electron can vary in physical size without affecting the electrodynamic action. The graviton cannot. If the volume of the graviton contracts very slightly, then the continuum can fill the space vacated, stay uniform, and allow the electron or other charges in the electromagneitc reference frame to expand slightly. The electrodynamic effects of the continuum are not affected by the change in physical size of the particles in the matter frame, as we have shown by reference to Fig. 18. The electrodynamic effects are augmented by any change in size of the graviton, because there is no compensating continuum flow past the graviton. It follows that if the graviton is squeezed into a smaller volume it will generate an electrodynamic effect in the continuum. The graviton, having a charge e, will add energy if this charge is squeezed into less space. Hence, energy added to the graviton system can lead to a related electrodynamic effect. The mutually-parallel nature of the electrodynamic action for two such events implies, by our law of electrodynamics, a mutual attraction between the two energy disturbances. Thus, if we can match the mass-energy of the electron or other matter present in the electromagnetic reference frame with that stored on the graviton system, we can argue that there will be mutual attraction between matter proportional to the product of the masses interacting. This can all be formulated.

To relate the size and energy of the graviton we will use the classical formula:

$$E = 2e^2/3x \tag{52}$$

This has been suggested by J. J. Thomson and will be discussed later in this work, but it can be justified independently of J. J. Thomson's argument as being the self-energy E of the electric field of a charge e confined within a sphere of radius x, when the charge distribution assures a uniform field energy density or pressure within the sphere.

If E increases by dE, x is reduced and there will be a graviton volume contraction $4\pi x^2 dx$. The value of dE/dx is $-2e^2/3x^2$ so the volume contraction can be estimated in terms of dE. The effect is to modify the electrodynamic current element by $\sigma u/c$ times this volume contraction or:

$$(6\pi x^4 \sigma/e^2)(u/c)dE \tag{53}$$

where u is the velocity of the continuum relative to the electro-magnetic or matter frame.

Two such current elements at unit distance are mutually attracted by a direct action along the line joining them and in direct pro-portion to the product of two quantities such as (53). Therefore, identifying this force as gravitation and using the formula $E = Mc^2$ to relate energy and mass, we can write:

$$G = (6\pi x^4 \sigma uc/e^2)^2 \tag{54}$$

Given the mass of the graviton we would know x. This leaves for evaluation the velocity u and the charge density σ. Also we have to explain why dE has any relation to the mass of an element of interacting matter, because we have added as much energy to the graviton as we have mass-energy in the matter frame. The interesting point, however, is that we have a formula for G which offers scope for understanding the very weak nature of the gravitational force. G is proportional to x^8 and x is a very small distance.

The challenge confronting us is to determine these parameters in (54). It is a task which involves the full analysis of the lattice structure of the space medium, and therefore one which requires acceptance of a kind of aether. This causes us to pause to discuss Einstein's Special Theory of Relativity, because some regard this as refuting the aether concept. However, it is a profitable line of enquiry, as we shall see, and we do find an answer to the mass-energy connection between matter and gravitons.

Before concluding this chapter, we will interject a comment about the parameter u. The approach we took in coming to our electrodynamic formulations suggests that the speed of interacting charge should be low in relation to c. This restriction does not apply to the very small charge disturbances in the continuum. The reason is that the undisturbed continuum has a completely balanced interaction with other charge in the space medium. Electrodynamic forces due to the continuum charge arise when the continuum is disturbed by deflection past elements of matter or by secondary effects which matter has upon gravitons. Therefore, the relevant velocity is not that of the undisturbed speed of the continuum. It is the incremental velocity of the continuum deflected by the presence of matter. Bearing in mind that a vastly greater volume of continuum is disturbed than the small volume displacement at the graviton, we must expect this incremental velocity to be effectively quite small. On the other hand the current quantity involved is correctly specified by u in formula (54). Therefore, provided we are considering electrodynamic effects remote from the source and provided these arise from motion confined within a limited region, such as an oscillation, u can be as great as we please and could equal c without affecting the applicability of the result.

On a similar point note that one cannot expect electrodynamic effects to govern the self-actions of electric charge, whether gravitons or electrons, because such effects are only asserted over ranges set by the scale of the q charge structure. This we have to determine in order to evaluate σ. It will be shown that the spacing between the q charges is large enough not to affect the self-action of a charge by electrodynamic interaction.

3

The Structure of the Vacuum

Cosmic Radiation Anisotropy

Space devoid of matter provides a frame of reference for isotropic cosmic radiation. By measuring the local anisotropy of such radiation it is possible to determine motion relative to this cosmic frame. Radiometers carried by U-2 aircraft at altitudes of 20 km have detected a component of Earth motion through space of 390 ± 60 km/s. This was reported in October 1977* and its importance was rapidly recognized by the scientific press. 'Aether drift detected at last' was a headline in *Nature*, November 3, 1977, at p. 9. The May, 1978, issue of *Scientific American* featured an article on the same subject under the title: 'The Cosmic Background Radiation and the New Aether Drift'.

Meanwhile, conscious of previously reported data indicating anisotropy of cosmic background radiation, theoretical physicists have been examining ways of healing the wound inflicted on aether theories by the relativistic doctrine. Sciama, writing at p. 298 of the February 2, 1978, issue of *New Scientist*, gives cause for reviving aether theory. His title was 'The Ether Transmogrified' and his case for conciliation was founded upon the assertion:

> Of course if one is allowed to give the ether whatever properties are required to account for electromagnetic phenomena no difficulty with the (aether) concept need arise.

There is nothing new in this idea. Nobel prizewinner Dirac pointed out in the May, 1963, issue of *Scientific American* at p. 50 that one can overcome the difficulties of reconciling the idea of an aether and Einstein's theory. Einstein has said this too, but the fact remains that the need for an absolute universal frame of reference is denied

* G. F. Smoot, M. V. Gorenstein and R. A. Muller, *Phys. Rev. Lett.*, **39**, 898 (1977).

by Einstein's Theory of Relativity and it now appears that such a reference frame has been discovered.

The doctrines of relativity have been exercised to suppress those who have advocated belief in the aether medium, with the result that interest in experiments of the kind now performed by NASA in the United States has been slow to develop. The renewed interest in the aether medium which should now follow these recent developments could herald other discoveries which may have great practical consequences. It is timely, therefore, to examine this mysterious vacuum through which we move at phenomenal speed and speculate a little on its properties in the light of modern experimental evidence. We have, it would seem, arrived at the crossroads in science of which we were alerted by Dingle in his famous book attacking relativity.*

The fundamental issue confronting us is that an experiment performed in the late nineteenth century showed that electromagnetic radiation in the laboratory vacuum was referenced on a frame moving with the Earth in its motion about the Sun. Such motion is at a speed of 30 km/s, compared with the speed of light of 300,000 km/s. This discovery thwarted the beliefs of scientists in the universal aether medium, supposedly providing the medium governing the speed of light anywhere in the universe. So perplexing was this problem that it paved the way for a new philosophical approach based upon the principle that the physics perceptible to any non-accelerated observer will never permit him to measure his speed without taking bearings upon a world external to his local system. Einstein's theory was built upon such a principle and has had amazing success. Yet Einstein's theory has not lived up to the expectations of many physicists. Einstein died having failed to accomplish a task he had struggled with for decades, that of unifying field theory to relate electromagnetic and gravitational interactions. Furthermore, in spite of the successes of Dirac, there has been insufficient connection established between quantum physics and relativity and it is difficult to see scope for any significant connections between relativity and the new particle physics.

Relativity may have passed its heyday and the case for reviving belief in the aether, now forced upon us by the cosmic radiation experiments, provides the stimulus for progress in physics along new non-relativistic tracks. The first task is to reconcile the detection of the background reference frame governing cosmic radiation with

* H. Dingle, *Science at the Crossroads*, Brian and O'Keefe, London, 1972.

the experiments on light propagation which helped to launch Einstein's theory. A clue is provided by the opening words of this chapter. 'Space devoid of matter' provides the cosmic frame of reference. What is different about the two experimental facts which we have just put in conflict? Simply that one involves the *speed* of radiation and the other the *intensity* of radiation. Speed is measured locally in the near presence of matter. Intensity based upon the assumption of the cosmic isotropy is measured locally too, but is a measure of radiation intensity in surrounding space undisturbed by matter. Here lies the key.

In empty space devoid of matter and not disturbed by nearby matter there is a universal cosmic reference frame relative to which electromagnetic waves travel at a constant and universal speed. Let us term this the 'C-frame'. In the laboratory environment even vacuous space might somehow be affected by the near presence of enveloping matter in motion relative to the surrounding C-frame. There could be disturbance affecting the properties of the space medium permeating the local vacuum. Here we know that the electromagnetic reference frame somehow adopts the observer's laboratory frame of reference so that the speed of light is independent of the linear motion of the laboratory and is constant in all directions. We may term this local electromagnetic reference frame the 'E-frame'. The E-frame and the C-frame become identical in the absence of matter.

In outer space it appears that the cosmic radiation is isotropic in the C-frame. Thus the intensity of this radiation traversing the Earthly laboratory will be isotropic relative to the surrounding C-frame. But the motion of the laboratory through space will mean that the energy detectors will sense an anisotropy in this radiation measured relative to the laboratory. This is so notwithstanding the fact that the speed of propagation of such radiation through the Earth system is rendered isotropic relative to the Earth's own E-frame.

Fig. 19 illustrates the hypothesis adopted. The Earth system moves through space at velocity V and causes disturbance of the permeating space medium by which the E-frame also travels at velocity V. Enveloping this there is undisturbed space in which the same medium provides a universal reference frame, the C-frame, which is similar in character to the E-frame but which is also the reference frame for motion such as V.

According to the old-fashioned aether hypothesis, the C-frame is the only frame of reference and would permeate the Earth as well. According to the Theory of Relativity, the only reference frames of relevance are those local to individual observers. In effect, with relativity there is a multiplicity of E-frames but no C-frame.

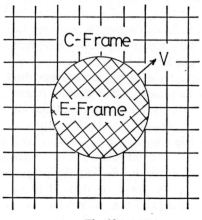

Fig. 19

It is true to say that much of physics can be described in relativistic terms without reference to the C-frame and the universal aether thereby implied, but it is wrong to deny the existence of such an aether in the light of the cosmic radiation experiments.

The discerning reader will recognize from Fig. 19 that what is proposed is a kind of 'aether drag' and will question the position of the boundary between the Earth's E-frame and the enveloping C-frame. Also there is the question of whether the E-frame rotates. Called to mind are problems of stellar aberration and Lodge's experiment* in which there was no evidence of drag on light propagation around a circuital path in the space between two rapidly rotating steel discs.

The boundary question will be left for a later chapter,† but we will deal here with Lodge's experiment and then come to the aberration issue. The null result of Lodge's experiment was taken as proving that there was no effect on the speed of light due to the motion of nearby matter. This is deemed to disprove aether drag.

* O. Lodge, *Phil. Trans. Roy. Soc.*, **184**, 727 (1893).
† See discussion on geomagnetism in Chapter 8.

But consider the consequences had a positive result been found. It would have meant that light speed was referenced on the frame rotating with the discs. Then an observer rotating with the discs would, in his frame, have been unable to detect his rotation by optical reference to the vacuum in his vicinity. Such a result would have been more in keeping with the relativistic hypothesis than with the idea of aether. In fact, the null result bears only upon aether drag in the sense of rotation and only then upon the drag of the electromagnetic reference frame. The word 'aether' conjures in our minds something more tangible than a mere frame of light reference and Lodge's experiment in no way proves that something tangible does not rotate with the discs.

The null result was consistent with the possibility of an observer rotating with the discs actually measuring his speed of rotation by optical tests based upon the non-rotational property of the vacuum. It became possible to measure speed of rotation in an absolute sense by interferometer techniques. The null result was a pointer that tests to detect rotary motion within a fixed aether medium should prove positive. The fixed aether concept need only stand refuted in respect of the failure to detect truly translational motion.

Reverting now to the E-frame theory, we see from Lodge's experiment that the E-frame cannot rotate, and yet, as will be shown, this does not deny rotation of structure constituting an aether and such rotation is important in defining the existence of separate E-frames.

Many optical experiments involving rotating apparatus and sensitive to the non-rotating vacuum frame have been performed. A modern development is found in the ring laser gyro. One of the earliest reported experiments was that of Sagnac* involving a ring interferometer on a rotating disc.

There is, in fact, a degree of conflict in certain experimental evidence involving speed of light measurements and bearing upon relativity. Simply stated, the experiments all give results in accord with the following statement:

Light in vacuum is propagated at a speed which is independent of direction when measured relative to an inertial reference frame.

The problem is that our measurements require this inertial reference frame to be, in some cases, a frame located by the centre of the Earth

* G. Sagnac, *Comptes Rendus*, **157**, pp. 708 and 1410 (1913).

and, in other cases in which the test apparatus is rotating, a frame referenced by the structure of the apparatus itself. The consequences of this are very perplexing and the Theory of Relativity does not provide an adequate answer because it gives no basis for distinguishing the inertial frame to be used when applying the Principle of Relativity.

It has long been recognized that physical phenomena dependent upon rotation can highlight weaknesses in relativity theory. Philosopher Alfred North Whitehead in his work 'The Principle of Relativity with Applications to Physical Science' wrote:*

> The effects of rotation are among the most widespread phenomena of the apparent world. . . . Rotation is the stronghold of those who believe that in some sense there is an absolute space to provide a framework of dynamical axes. . . . The Einstein theory in explaining gravitation has made rotation an entire mystery.

In his work 'An Enquiry Concerning the Principles of Natural Knowledge', Whitehead† discusses the problem of the Earth's rotation and the centrifugal effect which develops the Earth's equatorial bulge. He poses the question: 'But rotating relatively to what?', and writes:

> It has been asserted that after all the fixed stars are essential, and that it is the rotation relatively to them which produces the bulge. But surely this ascription of the centrifugal force on the Earth's surface to the influence of Sirius is the last refuge of a theory in distress. . . . The more natural deduction is to look on the result as evidence that the theory of any empty space is an essential impossibility. Accordingly the absoluteness of direction is evidence for the existence of the material ether. . . Thus space expresses mutual relationships of parts of the ether, as well as the parts of the earth.

The Michelson–Morley experiment dates back to 1887 and is very well known. It is essentially a test involving a four-way propagation of light, two opposite ways in each of two orthogonal directions. The apparatus was calibrated by measuring the change in a light interference pattern resulting when the system is turned through

* This work appears in A. N. Whitehead's *An Anthology*, Cambridge University Press, 1953, p. 356.
† See p. 183 of Whitehead's *An Anthology*.

90° to interchange the effects of aether drift between the two measurement paths.

Assuming that light travels at a fixed speed in space, this experiment should have yielded at least an indication of the 30 km/s motion of the Earth about the Sun. No such effect was observed and, as Joos* demonstrated many years after the earliest experiments, no aether slip can be detected by this method, at least to within 1·5 km/s.

The experiment demonstrated that, within the limits of a few km/s, the speed of light measured in the laboratory is the same in all directions. The interesting question then is whether this speed depends upon the Earth's rotation. The laboratory is carried about 30,000 km every day in its motion about the Earth's axis for most of our experimental sites and a speed detection of 0·3 km/s is necessary to sense this rotation.

The Michelson–Gale–Pearson experiment is almost unknown. Shankland† has recently reminded us of its importance. Michelson gave an early account of the theory and argued the possibility of detecting the effects of the Earth's rotation through an aether‡ and finally came to perform the experiment§ in the years 1923–25. This involves the four-way propagation of light around a rectangular light path. Two opposite sides of the rectangle lie along different lines of the Earth's latitude. Since the Earth rotates light should travel at different speeds along different lines of latitude if the idea of an aether is tenable. In this experiment the apparatus remained fixed to the Earth. There was no independent rotation. A calibration reference for the measurement utilized a light beam travelling along the path in the opposite direction to that of the test beam.

The experiment gave exactly the result predicted on fixed aether theory. It was possible to detect the rotation of the Earth by measuring its effect on light speed within a vacuum enclosed by apparatus rotating with the Earth.

Here was a surprising conflict with the results of the earlier Michelson–Morley experiment. It seemed that aether theory suited rotation detection but could not account for the non-detection of linear motion, whereas relativity satisfied the latter and was not

* G. Joos, *Ann. der Physik*, **7**, 385 (1930).
† R. S. Shankland, *Physics Today*, April, 1974, p. 37.
‡ A. A. Michelson, *Phil. Mag.*, **8**, 716 (1904).
§ A. A. Michelson, H. G. Gale and F. Pearson, *Astrophys. Jour.*, **61**, 140 (1925).

disturbed because it was generally silent on the former. These optical phenomena were the province of Einstein's Special Theory of Relativity and that concerns effects in non-rotating frames of reference.

A null result in the Michelson–Gale–Pearson experiment would have supported aether drag theory and could have helped the Theory of Relativity in dealing with the problem raised by Whitehead. It is one thing to look to distant stars as mediating between matter on Earth to help account for inertial properties in a way linked with gravitation. It is quite another matter to expect distant stars to affect the speed of propagation of light between two points on the Earth's surface, especially if this speed changes with latitude.

There is a tendency to dismiss this very important experiment as being a mere extension of the earlier Sagnac experiment, but it has far greater importance because the rotating reference frame for the experiment is the Earth itself.

Another very important experiment of this kind became possible once the maser was developed. It was no longer necessary to compare speed of light measurements at two latitudes. Instead of rotation being detected it became possible to test directly whether the east–west speed of light differs from the west–east speed. In the experiment reported in 1958 by Townes[*] working in collaboration with Cedarholm, Bland and Havens, the relative frequency of two beam-type maser oscillators with oppositely directed beams was used to test directly this speed difference. The test was a two-way test affording a first order measurement of v/c, where v is the speed of the apparatus through the aether and c denotes the speed of light. Calibration involves rotating the apparatus through 180° to interchange the beam directions. A measured 20 cps beat frequency would have indicated an aether drift of 30 km/s, assuming an appropriate thermal molecular velocity for the masers. In fact there was a consistent beat frequency measured of 1·08 cps which only varied about 0·05 cps during the day, that is during the full rotation of the Earth. This minimal variation throughout the 24 hour period gave affirmative evidence that the Earth's linear motion through space defies detection. The measured steady beat signal could indicate an aether drift about the Earth's axis of rotation of up to about 1·5 km/s. It was not so interpreted because the authors felt it to be due

* J. P. Cedarholm, G. F. Bland, B. L. Havens and C. H. Townes, *Phys. Review Lett.*, **1**, 342 (1958).

to magnetic effects which they had not compensated. Their results were therefore inconclusive. However, guided by the Michelson–Gale–Pearson experiment, one must expect a drift of about 0·3 km/s to be in evidence. The technique of this maser-beam experiment if refined to overcome the magnetic disturbance should permit the measurement of this 0·3 km/s drift, bearing in mind the degree of accuracy reported for the variable component of the beat signal. Such a measurement would be a direct speed measurement and not a measure of speed of rotation.

An experiment of this kind would be very crucial to the validity of the Theory of Relativity. Suppose, for example, that the Earth's west–east motion could be measured as a direct speed quantity by these optical tests. Einstein's theory is then refuted because the speed of light is no longer constant relative to the observer. After all, the observer will have just measured his speed relative to the non-rotating reference frame centred in the Earth's axis by assuming that light speed is referenced in that frame and not one moving with him. It would really be no use arguing that the measurement of 0·3 km/s attributable to his motion about a remote axis does not count owing to it not being a non-accelerated linear motion. The failure to detect the Earth's 30 km/s motion about the remote Sun has been attributed to relativity. Yet this motion is circuital and therefore accelerated.

It is of interest to mention that lasers have been used in a four-way ring configuration to measure Fresnel drag, whether in solid, liquid or even gaseous media. In a paper* dated 1964 which described such apparatus it was stated:

> The effect of Earth rotation was significant, as could be demonstrated by velocity reversal of the moving media, and all data points were accordingly adjusted.

One may wonder, therefore, why the implicit effect of sensitivity to motion through the light reference frame has not been seized upon to demonstrate the invalidity of Einstein's theory.

An answer to this may come from the experiments which have shown that aether drift in the laboratory can be measured to a few metres per second and demonstrated as non-existent. However, these experiments either depend upon laser technology (discussed later)

* W. M. Macek, J. R. Schneider and R. M. Salamon, *Jour. Appl. Phys.*, **35**, 2557 (1964).

or require a rotation of the test apparatus about an axis within the confines of the laboratory. At this stage, it is noted that there is a difference between the two rotating systems depicted in Fig. 20.

Optical experiments by observer A spinning with a rotating platform at speed v_1 about its axis may detect this speed v_1 but not his speed v_2 about the Earth's axis. Nor, similarly, will observer B moving with the Earth about the Earth's axis be able to detect the Earth speed v_3 about the Sun, but observer B could well be able to

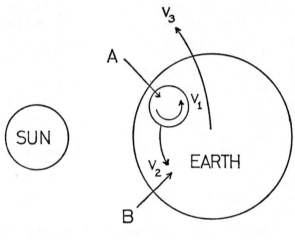

Fig. 20

detect his speed v_2 about this Earth axis. In the terminology developed earlier in this chapter we may say that rotating apparatus has developed in its own E-frame which moves within the larger E-frame of the Earth.

Thus a very important experiment on aether drift was proposed by Ruderfer* and performed by Champeney, Isaak and Khan.† It depends upon the Mossbauer effect and uses a gamma radiation source located at the central axis of a rapidly rotating table. The speed at which radiation is propagated from the source and measured relative to the axis is assumed to be subject to aether drifting past the apparatus. An absorber at the periphery of the table rotates at

* M. Ruderfer, *Phys. Review Lett.*, **5**, 191 (1960).
† D. C. Champeney, G. R. Isaak and A. M. Khan, *Proc. Phys. Soc.*, **85**, 583 (1965).

speed about the axis and senses the distorted wave radiation pattern emitted relative to the axis. The result should be a first-order one way sensing of aether drift. In fact none is detected in excess of a few metres per second. The experiment shows that the radiation travels at the same speed in different directions measured relative to the axis of the apparatus.

Although such experiments are deemed to have dispelled all credibility in the aether hypothesis and the scope for detecting motion through the reference medium for light propagation, the fact remains that Einstein's theory is on shaky foundation on the evidence of the optical detection of Earth rotation. More experiments involving apparatus sharing only the Earth's rotary motion are required.

A particularly relevant experiment, using laser interferometry is on record in 1976.* It gave such accurate null indications that the west–east motion of the laboratory due to Earth rotation was also nullified. This seems to refute the author's thesis, but it also seems anomalous having regard to the detection of rotation by using the ring laser gyro. Silvertooth, who performed this experiment, was led to interpret it as evidencing an aether interaction which implied an empirical reformulation of the Doppler Effect. However, it is submitted that the true answer to this anomaly lies in a basic deficiency in methods relying upon lasers as independent light sources when performing tests based upon interference effects.

In the ring laser gyro the optical interference path is intrinsic to the laser. The mirror system, which is essential to the laser, is the mirror system having an optical path sensitive to the speed of rotation. The laser frequency in this gyro device is therefore dependent upon the speed of rotation. Now, if the laser frequency depends upon the state of motion of the laser through the light-reference medium, we have to be very careful about using lasers in Michelson-type experiments. If the hypothetical basis for the experiment is that the apparatus is assumed somehow to be moving relative to the light-reference frame, then the effect of this same motion upon laser operation must be considered.

Since 1958, when the experiment by Cedarholm *et al.* was reported, the use of masers has given way to laser techniques. The above-mentioned 1976 experiment presented a refinement by superimposing the beams of two free-running lasers in oppositely-directed paths. Two semi-transparent photo-cathode detectors were placed some

* E. W. Silvertooth, *Applied Optics*, **15**, 1100 (1976).

50 cm apart along the axis of the interfering beams. These interrogated and compared the beat frequencies detected at the two locations. Theoretically, given stable laser frequencies, any motion through the light-reference frame would be directly related to a phase shift between the beat signals sensed. Silvertooth calculated a phase shift of some 79 complete cycles to correspond to the Earth's orbital velocity of 30 km/s. Thus a phase shift of this order was to be expected in rotating the apparatus through 90° at a certain time of day and given appropriate alignment of the apparatus. In spite of the very high sensitivity of this apparatus no phase shift was detected. The writer has questioned the author of this experiment and is assured that there was not the slightest trace of phase shift, meaning that even the 0·3 km/s west–east speed of Earth rotation was obscured.

Silvertooth's interpretation was that the frequencies of the interfering beams were themselves dependent upon velocity relative to a preferred frame. Hence he was led to propose an optical aether drift experiment which is currently under way at the University of Arizona Optical Sciences Center. Let us, instead, examine how motion could affect the laser directly. The amplification properties of the laser depend upon a resonance of reflected light waves and so depend upon the optical path within the laser. This must be an integral multiple of wave-lengths at the laser frequency. If the distance between the mirrors in the laser is fixed then it is only if the speed of light propagation over the return journey changes that we may expect the laser frequency to change.

For motion at velocity v along the laser axis, the speed of light is $c - v$ in one direction and $c + v$ in the other, c being the speed of light in the preferred frame. This makes an average speed of $1 - (v/c)^2$ times the speed of light c. For a fixed wave-length this corresponds to a frequency proportional to $1 - (v/c)^2$. The analysis is, indeed, analogous to that used as the basis for the Michelson–Morley experiment. It means that using a laser source moving in the direction of the laser axis we may expect the conventional Doppler equation for the frequency of a moving light source, as seen by a fixed observer, to be modified from a form proportional to $c/(c \pm v)$ to the inverse $(c \pm v)/c$. The ratio is the above parameter $1 - (v/c)^2$.

The alternative is to recognize that if lasers are used for Michelson–Morley type experiments or direct interferometer tests of the kind outlined above, the frequency of the lasers will adjust to the reorientation of the apparatus exactly to cancel any effect due to motion through the light-reference frame. The null result becomes an inevitable consequence.

It may then be argued that any experiment purporting to use lasers in an interferometer to disprove the idea of motion through the aether is inconclusive. Note, however, that this conclusion might well be different if the speed of light for the many reflections of the light within the laser is very different from that associated with the primary apparatus. For example, if the light path of the apparatus is in air and that of the laser is in, say, a ruby, then c would not be the same for the main apparatus and the ruby laser. The cancellation of effects related to the speed v would only be partial and v might well be detected. It is accordingly suggested that the Silvertooth experiment should be repeated using ruby lasers in order to establish whether optical tests referenced on the vacuum medium can directly sense the 0·3 km/s speed of the Earth's rotation about the Earth's axis. In contrast with the Michelson–Gale–Pearson experiment of 1925, this would be a measurement of speed rather than rate of rotation. A positive result seems very likely and it might have rather dire consequences to the confidence we can place in one of the basic tenets of the Theory of Relativity.

It is submitted that the concept of the E-frame as providing a non-rotating reference frame adapting to the linear motion of local matter is viable. It remains, of course to explore the structure of this E-frame, but first it seems appropriate to examine other optical evidence supporting relativity.

The Transverse Doppler Effect

Historically the null result of the Michelson–Morley experiment was explained shortly after its discovery, by the contraction hypothesis of Fitzgerald and Lorentz. The apparatus was deemed to contract in proportion to the factor $(1 - v^2/c^2)^{\frac{1}{2}}$ in its direction of motion at speed v. Lorentz modified his theory in 1904, reacting to the 1903 Trouton–Noble experiment (as discussed in Chapter 1) and the null detection of double diffraction by Rayleigh* and Brace.† He introduced time dilation in addition to contraction. These ideas also appear in Einstein's theory from 1905 onwards.

* Lord Rayleigh, *Phil Mag.*, **4**, 678 (1902).
† D. B. Brace, *Phil. Mag.*, **7**, 317 (1904).

In 1932 an experiment by Kennedy and Thorndike was reported.* It was similar to the Michelson–Morley experiment but required the optical arms of the interferometer to be of different length. It gave a null result and thereby indicated that if contraction was to be relied upon to explain the null Michelson–Morley result then there must also be a modification of the frequencies emitted by atoms producing the light source. The frequency had to be proportional to $(1 - v^2/c^2)^{\frac{1}{2}}$. The paper by Kennedy and Thorndike was deemed to verify the concept of time dilation and so one of the basic tenets of Einstein's theory.

Dingle, in discussing the Kennedy and Thorndike experiment in his 1940 book *The Special Theory of Relativity*,† declares that it is possible to interpret its null result as a Fitzgerald contraction plus a modification of the frequency emitted by atoms 'produced by their motion through the ether'. But he says this would involve ad hoc assumptions as there is no other evidence that such a phenomenon exists at all. In fact, Ives and Stilwell (1938, 1941) provided the experimental evidence that motion affects the optical frequencies emitted by atoms.‡ This has been taken as direct evidence of time dilation and as support for Einstein's theory. Thus, although the introduction of the E-frame concepts makes contraction and time dilation irrelevant as an explanation of the Kennedy and Thorndike null observation, the experiments of Ives and Stilwell in demonstrating what is termed the transverse Doppler effect are regarded as proof supporting the Theory of Relativity.

Now it is the concept of time dilation which is so difficult for many sceptics to accept. Yet this concept appears to have direct experimental support from three different aspects. Firstly, there are the direct optical measurements of transverse Doppler effect on atoms moving at high speeds. Secondly, there is the so-called 'thermal red shift', a transverse Doppler effect appearing in the emission of gamma rays by atomic nuclei and detected in Mossbauer experiments. Thirdly, there are experiments showing that the lifetime of mu-mesons increases with their speed.

In the face of such evidence it is hardly surprising that physicists can turn a blind eye to the open question left from the inconclusive

* R. J. Kennedy and E. M. Thorndike, *Physical Review*, **42**, 400 (1932).
† Published by Methuen. See p. 20.
‡ H. E. Ives and G. R. Stilwell, *Jour. Opt. Soc. Am.*, **28**, 215 (1938) and **31**, 369 (1941).

maser-beam experiments discussed above. It seems so improbable
that relativity could fail such a basic test. Yet, it only needs one
such failure for the whole theory to collapse. In this event, how
can we deal with the evidence giving independent support for time
dilation?

One of the tests above has a ready answer. It is to be found in a
book by Wertheim.* He first shows how the relativistic formulation
for the transverse Doppler effect is verified by affording an explanation for an extraneous effect which appeared in a Mossbauer
experiment. It appears as a red shift of the gamma quantum emitted
by the source and manifested in dependence upon temperature.
Then Wertheim goes on to give an entirely separate explanation
based solely upon use of the energy-mass relation $E = Mc^2$. The same
result is obtained without any use of the time dilation theory.
Wertheim concludes his account in favour of time dilation by discussing the 'twin paradox', one of the perplexing consequences of
time dilation, but in this connection relies essentially upon the
experimental evidence provided by meson decay.

Encouraged by this, let us ask whether the spectral emission by
atoms can be expected to be modified by motion. We need then to
examine the nature of the Rydberg constant R. Is this a speed-
dependent constant? Rc has the dimensions of frequency and R is
formulated as:

$$R = 2\pi^2 m e^4 / h^3 c \qquad (55)$$

where m is electron mass, e is electron charge, h is Planck's constant
and c is the speed of light in vacuo.

It is conventional to regard e, h and c as invariant, whereas m is
known to increase with speed in proportion to $(1 - v^2/c^2)^{-\frac{1}{2}}$. On this
account we would expect the value of R to increase with speed v,
whereas, for frequency subject to relativistic time dilation, R should
decrease in proportion to $(1 - v^2/c^2)^{\frac{1}{2}}$. Here then is an interesting
problem.

The answer emerges as soon as we remember how R is derived.
Rhc is an energy and, theoretically, it is the difference between an
electric interaction energy $4\pi^2 m e^4 / h^2$ and a kinetic energy $2\pi^2 m e^4 / h^2$.
If only this kinetic energy term is affected by the change of speed
whilst the interaction energy term remains unaffected then the mass

* G. K. Wertheim, *Mossbauer Effect: Principles and Applications*, Academic
Press, New York, 1964, p. 32.

increase only applies to the latter formulation. The Rydberg constant would then increase with speed v in proportion to:

$$2 - (1 - v^2/c^2)^{-\frac{1}{2}} \tag{56}$$

For small v/c this factor given by (56) is very close to the expression corresponding to time dilation $(1 - v^2/c^2)^{\frac{1}{2}}$.

But why should we suppose that the electric interaction energy does not exhibit mass increase with speed? Surely all energy has mass which is augmented by the mass attributable to its kinetic energy. Curiously, this is by no means certain. Although it is well established that inertial mass and gravitational mass are equivalent to a very high order of accuracy, there is no certain equivalence between mass and energy. The formula $E = Mc^2$ is a statement that a mass M has association with an energy E but its derivation is by no means an assurance that all energy exhibits mass. In discussing the experimental evidence favouring equivalence, Dicke* stresses that his conclusions depend upon the *assumption* of the equivalence of inertial mass and energy. This is a very important point, particularly as energy has different forms.

For example, kinetic energy and the rest mass energy of a particle are intimately associated with the inertial property and the derivation of $E = Mc^2$. Here the mass-energy equivalence must be rigorously valid. However, the mutual energy of interaction between the proton and the electron in the hydrogen atom is less evidently connected with its own inertial property. This two body system has its proton and electron in motion about their common centre of gravity and the electric interaction energy shares this same centre of gravity. If the mass property is somehow nucleated by electric charge it may only be the self energy of such charges that constitutes mass-energy. Indeed, collectively all the interaction energy present locally may be the determining influence which provides the local inertial frame. This is speculation, just as the supposition that interaction energy may have mass is mere assumption. It is, however, speculation encouraged by Brillouin.† He discusses the location of the mass ascribed to the interaction energy between an electron in a box and a charge on the box. He argues that none of this interacting energy

* R. H. Dicke, *The Theoretical Significance of Experimental Relativity*, p. 7. Blackie, London, 1964.

† L. Brillouin, *Relativity Reexamined*, Academic Press, New York, 1970, pp. 14 and 24.

can affect the mass of the electron in the box. In the same work he shows that it is conventional to disregard the movement of the 'external potential energy', the interaction energy of our argument, when considering inertial properties. He may well refer to this as a 'strange situation'. However, it is less strange when we see the result deduced above. It has led us to the time dilation formula without there being any need for time to dilate. When an atom is moving at high speed its spectral emission shifts simply because the energy quanta released are reduced. This is not time dilation in the sense intended by Einstein.

We have, however, a proposal which may yet be tested to distinguish between the relativistic theory and that just proposed. When v/c approaches unity it becomes possible to distinguish between (56) and the relativistic formula. Note the difference between the two expressions:

$$2 - (1 - v^2/c^2)^{-\frac{1}{2}} = 1 - \tfrac{1}{2}(v/c)^2 - 0.375(v/c)^4 \dots$$
$$(1 - v^2/c^2)^{0.5+k} = 1 - \tfrac{1}{2}(v/c)^2 - k(v/c)^2 - 0.125(v/c)^4 \dots$$

An experiment is needed to measure k to check whether it is zero as required by relativity or whether it has a positive value of approximately $0.25(v/c)^2$, as indicated by the theory just developed.

Mandelberg and Witten[*] in their experiments with hydrogen atoms used a value of v/c of less than 0.01 and found that $0.5 + k$ was 0.498 ± 0.025. Snyder and Hall,[†] working with neon atoms, aim for much higher accuracy and have already reported $0.5 + k$ as 0.502 ± 0.003. Snyder and Hall seek to detect the existence of a 'preferred frame' by a speed-of-light anisotropy measurement which could also account for a finite value of the factor k, but which, if detected, would nevertheless disturb the basis for relativity.

It is submitted that the spectral frequency shifts found when atoms move at high speed are not convincing evidence of time dilation. It then remains to consider the third support, that provided by the meson lifetime.

Here it is observed that Einstein's theory does not explain the reason by meson decay. Meson lifetime is not calculated by applying relativity. Given that a meson at rest has a definite mean lifetime, the observation that this increases with speed v in proportion to

---

[*] H. I. Mandelberg and L. Witten, *Jour. Opt. Soc. Am.*, **52**, 529 (1962).

[†] J. J. Snyder and J. L. Hall's researches are discussed in an editorial section in *New Scientist*, April 22, 1976, p. 184.

$(1-v^2/^2c)^{-\frac{1}{2}}$ was taken by those interested in relativity as endorsement for the proposition that time is dilated. It is also true to say that the energy of the meson increases owing to its speed in exactly this same proportion. Then, as Cullwick writes in his paper 'The Riddle of Relativity',[*]

> The reason for the decay of a meson is not known, but it is not unreasonable to suppose that its endurance in some way depends on its energy.

Meson lifetime should not be taken as proof of time dilation in these circumstances. Rather the evidence should be regarded as support for the so-called relativistic mass increase. Indeed, all the experiments which purport to support time dilation have ready explanation if one can accept the aether hypothesis plus the two facts which can be justified independently without recourse to the Theory of Relativity, namely the formula $E = Mc^2$ and the formula for increase of mass with speed. Cullwick in the above paper explains how these two formulae follow from a combination of Maxwell's theory and Newton's Third Law of Motion. We will consider a different justification in the next chapter.

Aberration

Stellar aberration, as discovered by Bradley, was understood in pre-Einstein times in terms of the motion of an Earthly observer through the fixed aether medium. The failure to detect the Earth's motion by the Michelson–Morley experiment then cast doubt on the aether explanation of aberration. Einstein[†] has asserted that the explanation of aberration as a result of relative motion is 'exceedingly simple'. But there are aspects of aberration which need special consideration as we progress towards more refined methods of optical measurement.

Born,[‡] in his book *Einstein's Theory of Relativity*, demonstrates the difficulty of using wave theory to account for a phenomenon as simple as aberration. He explains the need to consider motion of light energy as corpuscular in character. Born argued that light was not at all deflected by an aether wind, which then leaves open the

[*] E. G. Cullwick, *Bull. Inst. Phys.*, March, 1959, p. 55.
[†] A. Einstein, *Relativity*, Crown, New York, 1961, p. 49.
[‡] M. Born, *Einstein's Theory of Relativity*, Dover, 1962, p. 140.

question of whether there is an aether drag associated with the Earth. He also pointed out that Fresnel's theory gave very good account of experimental facts.

Curiously, however, light is deflected by the lateral motion, or rather the rotary lateral motion, of matter. Jones* has verified the lateral drag given by the Fresnel formula. He obtained very accurate confirmation. The lateral displacement δ of a ray of light traversing a rotating glass disc of thickness d and refractive index n was found to be:

$$\delta = dn(1 - 1/n^2)(v/c) \tag{57}$$

where v is the lateral speed of the disc and c is the speed of light in vacuo.

It is noted that in the classical electromagnetic theory of light propagation:

$$n^2 = 1 + \varphi \tag{58}$$

where φ is an expression representing the oscillating electrons within the refractive medium. φ will move with the medium. The unity term in (57) is a vacuum property and if this remains at rest we can regard the quantity $1 + \varphi$ as having an overall motion which is $\varphi/(1 + \varphi)$ that of φ. From (58) this is $(1 - 1/n^2)$, the factor used in (57). By supposing that as light traverses the medium laterally at speed c/n it is deflected in the direction of rotation of the medium at a rate equal to the Fresnel drag coefficient, we obtain the formula (57).

Yet it is not at all obvious why Fresnel drag should affect the *direction* of a light beam when, historically, it is only concerned with a change in the *speed* of light travelling in the line of motion of the refractive medium. Bearing in mind that the E-frame does not rotate, we can interpret this experiment by Jones as indicating that the motion of a refractive medium relative to the E-frame can cause lateral drag. The logic for this is that φ in (58) represents an electromagnetic disturbance and so must be referenced on an electromagnetic reference frame.

A question then of interest is what happens for a linear lateral motion? We know that the Earth carries its E-frame with it in its linear motion through space. If a refractive medium moves linearly with this E-frame there is no relative motion and we should not expect the presence of the refractive medium to cause any lateral drag deflecting a light beam. This is verified by an experiment

* R. V. Jones, *Proc. Roy. Soc. Lond.*, **A328**, 337 (1972).

performed by Airy, who found that a telescope filled with water and moving with the Earth about the Sun will give the same aberration observations as those of Bradley.

In accord with Born, we must interpret Bradley's aberration measurements as implying no lateral drag owing to the 'aether wind', or rather the lateral motion of the E-frame. Here is a very important clue to the content of the vacuum medium. The E-frame may have some tangible structure but, for some reason, its motion does not drag a light beam. We would expect the beam to be transported laterally by the E-frame. So what is happening? The answer appears to be that it is being transported forward by the E-frame and backwards by something moving in a counter-motion to the E-frame, with the result that it remains undeflected. Whereas the refractive medium had, in the Jones experiment, a unidirectional motion and could thereby impart momentum, the linear motion of the E-frame appears not to be able to communicate momentum, because there is a balance of linear momentum owing to the reverse flow of that 'something' associated with the E-frame.

The model we come to, in terms of the q charge system, is that the E-frame comprises a structured lattice of q charges which may move bodily through space. However, to avoid any build-up of q charge at the forward boundaries of such a system, when moving linearly, there is a migrant population of q charges in reverse flow through the lattice. The latter is like a gaseous medium flowing through the interstices within a moving solid, but assuring that the net linear momentum is zero. It seems then that the frame of reference for electromagnetic disturbance is set by the lattice system, and so the speed of light is referenced on this E-frame lattice, but the linear motion of the lattice cannot drag a light beam laterally.

It is rather perplexing that the rotation of the lattice appears not to result in a rotation of the E-frame and yet the linear motion of the lattice carries the E-frame with it. It would seem more consistent to look to the lattice properties to provide a structure having a degree of rigidity and capable of generating displacements which propagate at a fixed speed in a universal frame of reference. The rigidity could stem from the powerful electric interaction forces between the q charges and apply even though there may be a translation or rotation of a body of q charge having its own lattice structure.

Such rigidity might then permit us to make an analogy with solid materials by imparting to the vacuum medium a pressure modulus or energy density modulus P, which relates to the propagation speed c_1 by the formula:

$$c_1 = (P/\rho)^{\frac{1}{2}} \tag{59}$$

where ρ is the mass density of the lattice. Here c_1 is referenced on the universal frame.

In undisturbed space remote from matter c_1 will equal c, but, where we have a body of the lattice in linear motion at velocity v, some of the lattice substance will be shed to establish the counter-flow at velocity u and ρ in (59) will thereby be reduced, making c_1 larger than c. Write:

$$n = c/c_1 \tag{60}$$

where n is the refractive index in this region. Then, from (59) and (60) we see that n^2 is proportional to the mass density of the lattice.

We expect linear momentum of the vacuum medium to be zero and this means that if the proportion k of the lattice is shed to provide the balancing flow the following relation holds:

$$uk + v(1 - k) = 0 \tag{61}$$

Also: $$n^2 = 1 - k \tag{62}$$

Combining (61) and (62), we have:

$$u(1 - 1/n^2) = v \tag{63}$$

Now the expression given by (63) is the Fresnel drag coefficient and, as applied to the vacuum medium, it tells us that the speed of light within a linearly-moving lattice is augmented by the velocity v, that is by the velocity of the lattice. In other words, relative to the moving lattice the speed of light is the same in all directions, as we know it should be from the Michelson–Morley experiment. Hence, we are correct in saying that the E-frame can move linearly. On the other hand, for rotation there is no counterflow and no Fresnel drag, meaning that the E-frame does not rotate.

On this interpretation, we also find that the light from a star will not undergo any lateral deflection owing to the motion of the E-frame with the Earth. Hence we can apply the classical explanation to the problem of aberration.

It may seem to be highly speculative to devise a dual aether, in the sense that the vacuum has a structured particle form which can move within surrounding structure by dissolving at its forward boundaries and flowing back through the structure in a kind of gaseous form to reestablish structure at the rear. Yet, given that Nature's forces favour structure and that Nature insists on motion of structure within structure, there is very little alternative to the model presented. With this two-part aether we have a system able to develop a frame of electromagnetic reference which adapts to the linear motion of matter, and does this without demanding any linear momentum. The model is so simple that one wonders why it was not discovered in earlier times. Perhaps the answer lies in the fixed idea that the word 'aether' had conveyed in the period before the Michelson–Morley discovery. In the words of Campbell,* writing in 1913:

> This is the simple way out of the difficulties raised by the Michelson–Morley experiment. If from the beginning we had used a plural instead of a singular word to denote the system in which radiant energy is localised (or even a word which, like 'sheep', might be either single or plural), those difficulties would never have appeared. There has never been a better example of the danger of being deceived by arbitrary choice of terminology. However, physicists, not recognising the gratuitous assumption made in the use of the words 'the aether', adopted the second alternative; they introduced new assumptions.

Campbell meant here that they turned to relativity. Instead, and in some accord with Campbell's view, we have seen that the aether hypothesis can survive the experimental tests without recourse to the rather abstract concepts of relativity. The hypothesis of a structured vacuum component capable of motion to endow an observer's own system with its own electromagnetic reference frame overcomes the difficulties.

Happily, we have been led into other problems, which cause us to address issues beyond the scope of Einstein's theories. The most important of these is that, whereas we have argued that the linear motion of the E-frame with a structured lattice has no net linear momentum, there is the case to consider for which the lattice rotates, albeit without causing the E-frame to rotate. For lattice rotation the vacuum medium should exhibit angular momentum.

* N. R. Campbell, *Modern Electrical Theory*, Cambridge University Press, 2nd ed., 1913, p. 388.

We will come back to this in Chapters 8 and 9, particularly in relation to the lattice rotation with the Earth. Suffice it here to say that, whereas the Earth appears to share its rotation with the q charge lattice of the space medium, the mere rotation of apparatus such as that used by Champeney *et al.* for their Mossbauer tests does not mean that the coextensive charge lattice will rotate at the same speed as the apparatus. The lattice rotation is governed by an electrical inductive action and this imposes certain constraints, which nevertheless have interesting consequences and merit experimental exploration.

4

The Role of Energy

Relativistic Mass Increase

In the first two chapters of this work we have seen how electro-dynamics can be linked to gravitation and have derived Einstein's formula for gravitation without recourse to his General Theory of Relativity. It has been shown that, given this new approach to Einstein's law of gravitation, there is little of consequence in his General Theory. Then, in our third chapter, we have addressed the issues of the Michelson–Morley experiment and found that there is scope for reviving the aether concept and so questioning much of Einstein's Special Theory of Relativity, particularly the concept of time dilation. In doing this there has been reliance upon two of Einstein's famous laws, the energy-mass relation and the relativistic formula for increase of mass with speed. However, these were said to have justification in classical electromagnetic theory quite in-dependently of Einstein's theory. Our task is now to enlarge on this theme and show that $E = Mc^2$ has its origins in a very important energy conservation property.

At the outset it is stressed that experimental verification of $E = Mc^2$ is not proof of the Theory of Relativity. Einstein's theory dates from 1905. Einstein was not the first to theorize about the transmutability of energy and mass.

It was textbook knowledge in 1904 that electrons and positrons might mutually annihilate one another and create energy. In an article in *Nature* by Jeans* (1904) this mutual annihilation was proposed and argued to be a 'rearrangement of the adjacent aether structure'. Quoting from Jeans' paper:

There would, therefore, be conservation of neither mass nor material energy; the process of radioactivity would consist in an

* J. H. Jeans, *Nature*, **70**, 101, June 2, 1904.

increase of the material energy at the expense of the destruction of a certain amount of matter.

Jeans' ideas were mentioned in the 1904 book by Whetham*;

A more fundamental suggestion has been made by J. H. Jeans, who imagines that radio-activity may result from the coalescence of positive and negative electrons. On this idea, the energy of radio-active atoms is supplied by the actual destruction of matter.

This was before Einstein wrote on the $E = Mc^2$ subject and, of course, very much before Dirac theorized about the existence of the positron and the mutual annihilation of electrons and positrons. Simple dimensional analysis tells us that if energy and mass are interchangeable they must be related by a speed dimension squared. The early twentieth century physicists were seeking to understand how the Sun could pour out its energy for so many years and yet not appear to cool down. Here was their answer, but the speed parameter had to be very high. The connection was the speed of light c.

Quoting again from Whetham's 1904 textbook (p. 283):

Theory shows that, for a slowly moving corpuscle, the electric inertia outside a small sphere of radius a, surrounding the electrified particle, does not depend on the velocity, and is measured by $2e^2/3a$ where e is the electric charge of the particle. But when the velocity of light is approached, this electric mass grows rapidly; and, on the assumption that the whole of the mass is electrical, Thomson has calculated the ratio of the mass of a corpuscle moving with different speeds to the mass of a slowly moving corpuscle, and compared these values with the results of Kaufmann's experiments. In this remarkable manner has it been possible to obtain experimental confirmation of the theory that mass is an electrical or aethereal phenomenon.

Here we refer to physics as it was before Einstein presented his theory. Yet we speak today of relativistic mass increase of the electron as if we owe its justification exclusively to the principles first enunciated by Einstein.

* W. C. D. Whetham, *The Recent Development of Physical Science*, John Murray, London, p. 290, 1904.

It is of interest that Jeans,* writing in 1929, disclaimed the priority of his idea about mass-energy transmutability:

> More than twenty years ago I directed attention to the enormous store of energy made available by the annihilation of matter, by positively and negatively charged protons and electrons falling into and annihilating one another, thus setting free the whole of their intrinsic radiation. On this scheme neither energy nor matter had any permanent existence, but only a sort of sum of the two; each was, theoretically at least, convertible into the other.
>
> When I put forward this hypothesis, I thought I was advocating something entirely revolutionary and unheard-of, but I have since found that Newton had anticipated something very similar exactly two centuries earlier. In his *Opticks* (1704) we find:
> 'Query 30. Are not gross bodies and light convertible into one another; and may not bodies receive much of their activity from the particles of light which enter into their composition? The changing of bodies into light, and light into bodies, is very conformable to the course of Nature, which seems delighted with transmutations.'

In classical electromagnetic theory the electromagnetic momentum of a field is equal to the flow of energy through unit area in unit time divided by c^2. c is the speed of an electromagnetic wave in a vacuum. In attributing this knowledge to Sir J. J. Thomson, Wilson† goes on to show that, since energy can be converted from one kind to another while momentum is conserved, there must be general validity for:

$$E = Mc^2 \tag{64}$$

Here E is the total energy associated with a mass M. Then from this Wilson deduces the dependence of mass upon velocity v, obtaining the usual (so-called relativistic) formula:

$$M = M_0(1 - v^2/c^2)^{-\frac{1}{2}} \tag{65}$$

His analysis relied upon there being *no loss of energy by radiation*. Let a force F act on a particle of momentum Mv. Then:

$$Fdt = d(Mv) \tag{66}$$

* J. H. Jeans, *EOS or the Wider Aspects of Cosmogony*, Kegan Paul, Trench, Trubner, London, p. 36, 1929.
† H. A. Wilson, *Modern Physics*, 2nd ed., Blackie, London, p. 8, 1946.

where dt is a short interval of time. Write the amount of energy transferred in this short interval of time as dE, which from (64) is c^2dM. This is put equal to the work done by the force F to give:

$$Fvdt = c^2dM \qquad (67)$$

From (66) and (67):

$$v \, d(Mv) = c^2dM \qquad (68)$$

Multiply this by M:

$$(Mv)d(Mv) = c^2MdM \qquad (69)$$

Integrate (69):

$$(Mv)^2 = c^2M^2 + K \qquad (70)$$

where K is a constant.

Now write M as M_0 when v is 0:

$$M^2v^2 = c^2(M^2 - M_0^2) \qquad (71)$$

Rearranged this gives the formula (65). In fact, we have deduced the 'relativistic' mass formula from $E = Mc^2$ using simple Newtonian principles.

This rigorous mathematical treatment proves that the Einstein mass-energy formula and the relativistic mass formula are only compatible if there is no loss of energy by radiation due to acceleration. This is seemingly in direct contradiction to Wilson's derivation of $E = Mc^2$ in terms of energy transfer by electromagnetic radiation.

In this connection reference is made to a commentary by Krause[*] who discusses the thought experiment proposed in 1904 by Hasenohrl. This concerns the behaviour of electromagnetic radiation trapped by internal reflection within a lossless cavity. It is a method of explaining $E = Mc^2$ discussed by Lenard[†] and it has reappeared in the literature recently in a new form in the work of Jennison and Drinkwater.[‡] The point made by Krause is that, if $E = Mc^2$ is explained by associating mass properties with radiation, then there is incompatibility with the assumption that E is conserved and that energy is not dispersed by radiation. However, as Krause notes, if E is conserved as trapped radiation how can we be justified in using the formula $dE = c^2dM$, as we do in equation (67) above? If E is the total trapped energy in the wave system and it is constant, then we cannot suppose it to change. It becomes, therefore, difficult to

[*] American Journal of Physics, **43**, 459 (1975).
[†] P. Lenard, Physik, vol. 4, Lehmann's Verlag, Munich, p. 157 (1936).
[‡] Journal of Physics, **A, 10**, 167 (1977).

deduce the relativistic mass increase from Hasenohrl's thought experiment in such circumstances.

What is really needed is an explanation of $E = Mc^2$ which overcomes these difficulties and is itself based upon the assumption that there is no loss of energy by radiation. Einstein's method of deriving the formulae for the relativistic mass increase and the mass-energy relation also do not escape criticism on this issue of energy radiation. Relativity gives no comprehensive account of the radiation processes. Indeed, the numerous papers on the subject fail to provide a coherent treatment of the problem, as we shall see in the next section.

The author believes that the true interpretation for this paradox is that Nature assures an effective 'no radiation' condition for electric charges undergoing acceleration. Space is seething with energy in an equilibrium state. If there is radiation disturbing this equilibrium then energy must be fed back to radiating matter to restore the balance. Quantum electrodynamics may play a role in this. However, Einstein's theory provides inadequate physics, even with regard to its basic formulae (64) and (65) above.

Energy Radiation

The scientific literature abounds with confusion on this question of energy radiation by accelerated charge. One view is that of Stabler[*] who has suggested that an accelerated charge does not radiate energy but that, collectively with other charge, it may somehow participate in an energy radiation from the mutual field system. Aharoni[†] in a detailed text on Relativity has written at length on the subject of energy radiation by the accelerated electron, but has made it appear quite mysterious:

> The radiation, whether into the source or away from it, introduces an asymmetry in time, or a time arrow, and this cannot be explained in electromagnetic terms.

He then refers to the theories of Wheeler and Feynman (1945) and follows that by the treatments of Dirac (1938) and Rohrlich (1960), arriving at a point where he writes:

[*] R. C. Stabler, *Physics Letters*, **8**, 185 (1964).
[†] J. Aharoni, *The Special Theory of Relativity*, 2nd ed., Oxford University Press, pp. 186 and 198, 1965.

It is typical of the new situation that the law of causality in its strict classical form does not hold. Already a short time before a force is applied the electron begins accelerating and the acceleration begins to diminish a short time before the applied force is stopped (assuming that such a step force can be produced). The time in question ... is the time it would take an electromagnetic wave to cross an electron. It is possible to interpret this result by saying that the electron has finite size and that at the instant the fringe of the electron experiences a force, it is transmitted with infinite velocity through the electron (breakdown of ordinary space-time laws inside the electron).

Some argue that the Theory of Relativity is inconsistent with the radiation of energy by accelerated charge. For example, Weber* talks of the equivalence principle and annulling of gravitational fields by appropriate acceleration. In free fall within an elevator he says:

A body would move within it as though no gravitational field were present, and no observations made on the body could enable a distinction to be drawn between an inertial frame and the space inside the elevator. ... It is not clear that this will still be true if the body within the elevator is electrically charged.

Weber then refers to several papers discussing radiation by a point charge electron. The authors are Bondi and Gold (1955), DeWitt and Brehme (1960), Drukey (1949) and Fulton and Rohrlich (1960). After talking of the complication arising from the infinite self-energy of a point electron, Weber concludes:

It may be that when the internal structure of elementary particles is properly taken into account, a charged particle will be found to radiate and have a non-vanishing radiation reaction when falling in a uniform gravitational field. It would follow that by observing a charged and uncharged body falling freely we can distinguish by local measurements whether we are in an inertial frame or falling freely in a gravitational field. The equivalence principle then becomes merely a guide for the formulation of the equations of the gravitational field alone, and not a general law of nature.

* J. Weber, *General Relativity and Gravitational Waves*, Interscience Publishers, New York, 1961, p. 146.

It is evident from this that the radiation of energy by the accelerated electron is an enigma confronting Relativity. DeWitt and Brehme* in the abstract of their paper write:

The particle tries its best to satisfy the equivalence principle in spite of its charge.

But, surely, it might be more a question of the particle, not being a point charge with infinite mass, trying its best to conserve its charge in spite of its finite mass. The principle of equivalence, meaning the role which the inertial mass plays in being also the gravitating mass, seems rather too fundamental to be questioned due to energy radiation problems, particularly in view of the total lack of experimental evidence that a discrete accelerating electric charge radiates any energy continuously.

Far from being resolved with the progress of time, the problem gains momentum. Bonnor† drew attention to the implications of charge radiation in company with energy radiation. Wilkins‡ (1975) has discussed the paradox raised by Weber and, in accord with other writers, concluded that there can even be energy radiation by charges which are not moving. Meanwhile, the classical radiation problem has been addressed by Geodecke§ (1975), Moniz and Sharp** (1974) and Cohn†† (1975), the latter's work being challenged by Kapusta‡‡ (1976).

Reacting to Weber's comments, is it not better to accept the principle of equivalence and declare that an accelerated electron does *not* radiate energy? It is the simple answer and it is not a new idea. Referring to Pauli's contention that there is no energy radiation, Fulton and Rohrlich§§ wrote:

Is Pauli's proof in error? If it is correct and if therefore uniformly accelerated charges do not radiate energy, where does the proof of the well-known radiation formula, found in the standard textbooks, break down?

* B. DeWitt and R. W. Brehme, *Annals of Physics*, **9**, 220 (1960).
† W. B. Bonnor, *Nature*, **225**, 932 (1970).
‡ D. C. Wilkins, *Physical Review*, **D12**, 2984 (1975).
§ G. H. Geodecke, *Nuovo Cimento*, **30B**, 108 (1975).
** E. J. Moniz and D. H. Sharp, *Physical Review*, **D10**, 1133 (1974).
†† J. Cohn, *Nuovo Cimento*, **26B**, 47 (1975).
‡‡ J. Kapusta, *Nuovo Cimento*, **31B**, 225 (1976).
§§ T. Fulton and F. Rohrlich, *Annals of Physics*, **9**, 499 (1960).

We will examine this question in the next section. It will be shown that close to the accelerated charge there is an action which suggests that any radiation of energy is not sourced in charge itself. One could argue that the well-known formula breaks down because it depends upon the *assumption* that energy is radiated rather than being locally exchanged with the space medium. Long ago, Livens* (1926) has shown how Poynting's theory can be modified, without departing from formulae consistent with observation, to become a theory which:

> does not associate energy at all with the radiation, so that no question of its transference arises.

When Dirac† (1938) adapted the classical theory of energy radiation by accelerated charge to accommodate relativistic principles, he concluded:

> It would appear that we have a contradiction with the elementary ideas of causality.

It is appropriate, however, to note that Dirac relied to some extent upon the earlier ideas of Schott‡ (1915) who had shown that the work done by the accelerating field:

> is converted into kinetic energy as if there had been no radiation at all.

The price paid in linking radiation with this balance of energy between the interacting field system and the kinetic states was the introduction of a separate energy called 'acceleration energy'. In Schott's work this was based upon the action of a *mechanical aether*.

Grandy§ was another voice on the subject:

> There is no paradox in the Lorentz–Dirac theory of the classical electron. Nevertheless, the physical picture provided by the theory is somewhat unsatisfactory, because one does not completely understand the physical origin of the Schott energy. . . . Plainly, the problem is that a clear insight into the Schott energy is outside the scope of classical electrodynamics. No relief is to be found in

* G. H. Livens, *Theory of Electricity*, Cambridge University Press, 2nd ed., 1926.
† P. A. M. Dirac, *Proc. Roy. Soc.*, **A167**, 148 (1938).
‡ G. A. Schott, *Phil. Mag.*, **29**, 49 (1915).
§ W. T. Grandy, *Nuovo Cimento*, **65A**, 738 (1970).

quantum electrodynamics, either, which is totally unable to account for the structure of the electron. We must, therefore, wait for a satisfactory theory of fundamental particles, if one should ever emerge, in order to gain a more satisfying physical picture.

The problem of electromagnetic energy transfer by the radiation process is not satisfactorily answered in modern works of reference. How can energy be radiated continuously by acceleration and yet satisfy our belief that energy is transferred in quanta? The problem could involve the mere assumption implicit in the use of the Poynting vector, namely that energy is radiated. The supposition that a wave does carry energy at the speed of light is itself suspect. We associate particles with transfer of energy and particles never quite reach the speed of light. Photons are imagined to travel at the speed of light but deemed to transfer energy in quanta. The waves on the sea do not convey water along at the speed of the wave. The water present locally is disturbed to form the wave motion as the disturbance is communicated from adjacent water. Can it be that space is permeated by energy in a form which can be disturbed to give the appearance of something progressing through it at the speed of light? These are speculations which are unlikely to clarify the situation, but they need to be kept in mind.

The other argument is that energy is released in quanta but does not travel in quanta. The photon may be an event in which energy is released and disseminated throughout space by a dispersal unrelated to the wave radiation, but the reverse photon event by which energy is extracted from the space medium may be statistical in character. The energy might appear to travel at the speed of light but, in reality, it is added to the sea of energy in space and spreads gradually until equilibrium asserts balance. This equilibrium process coupled with the action of the spreading wave can seemingly induce a resonance in the space medium and transfer an energy quantum from the sea of energy present to the matter associated with the resonance condition.

Whatever conclusions are drawn on the question of energy radiation, it remains logical to regard the accelerated charge as a conservative element, preserving its energy on a shared basis with other interacting charge. If there is energy radiation in the field then it could be that the field medium itself is a whole seething sea of electric charges of the two polarities, all busy exchanging energy with matter. This must then be a two-way process, assuring that charge does not have any net radiation loss of energy when accelerated. It will be shown that, apart from the non-radiation condition reconciling the Einstein mass-energy formula and the relativistic mass formula, it can be the basis of explaining the nature of inertia and the actual derivation of $E = Mc^2$. This will be the subject of the next section.

First, however, it is appropriate to mention that in high energy collisions between electrons it has been verified experimentally that momentum is shared in accordance with dynamics based upon the relativistic mass formula, but only provided there is no loss of energy by radiation in the collison. This was firmly shown by Champion.*

Also, we should refer to Einstein's own argument. In his basic paper† 'On the Electrodynamics of Moving Bodies' there is the derivation of the relativistic energy equation:

$$E = Mc^2[(1 - v^2/c^2)^{-\frac{1}{2}} - 1]] \tag{72}$$

He argues:

As the electron is to be slowly accelerated, and consequently may not give off any energy in the form of radiation, the energy withdrawn from the electrostatic field must be put down as equal to the energy of motion of the electron.

This must raise questions about the relevance of the Larmor radiation formula.

Later in the same year Einstein‡ presented a second paper entitled 'Does the Inertia of a Body Depend upon its Energy Content?' His method of calculation relied upon three elements:

(1) the Maxwell–Hertz Equations for empty space,
(2) the Maxwellian expression for the electromagnetic energy of space, and
(3) the Principle of Relativity.

In a footnote it is observed that the principle of the constancy of the velocity of light is contained in Maxwell's equations. The energy content of an electromagnetic wave is introduced and Einstein arrives at the conclusion that the emission of energy E by radiation diminishes the mass of a body by E/c^2. He writes:

* F. C. Champion, *Proc. Roy. Soc.*, **A136**, 630 (1932).
† *Annalen der Physik*, **17**, 891 (1905).   ‡ Ibid., **18**, 639 (1905).

The fact that the energy withdrawn from the body becomes energy of radiation evidently makes no difference, so we are led to the more general conclusion that the mass of a body is a measure of its energy content.

The perplexing question we are left with is why energy radiation is needed to explain $E = Mc^2$ but energy radiation is expressly forbidden if we are to correlate $E = Mc^2$ with the formula for relativistic mass increase. Let us resolve this problem by showing how we can deduce $E = Mc^2$ from the very opposite viewpoint, the fact that there is no radiation of energy by accelerated charge.

The Energy-Mass Formula

Consider the problematic Larmor formula:

$$\frac{dE}{dt} = \frac{2e^2f^2}{3c^3} \tag{73}$$

and examine its derivation. It expresses the rate at which energy is radiated from an electric charge e when accelerated at the rate f.

The formula was founded upon the assumption that waves are developed by an accelerated charge and spread remote from the charge into empty space. Then, by the additional assumption that energy is carried by these waves, an energy radiation as given by the Larmor formula is obtained. The effects of the accelerating field are irrelevant at large distances and do not affect the waves. Accordingly, the accelerating field need not be considered in the classical derivation of the formula. It is this latter comment that attracts our attention in this critical examination.

Let us first summarize how the Larmor formula is derived using a textbook method attributed to J. J. Thomson. Refer to Fig. 21. At a point P in the wave zone distant ct from a charge e centred at O the electric field disturbance which gives the energy radiation is of the form:

$$\frac{ef\sin\theta}{c^3t} \tag{74}$$

Here θ is the angle between OP and the direction of an accelerating electric field V or acceleration f. The field given by (74) is at right angles to the electric field of e acting along OP.

The Larmor formula is deduced by integrating the energy density attributable to this field term (74) for an elemental volume $2\pi(ct)^2$ $\sin\theta\ cdt\ d\theta$ between the limits $\theta=0$ and $\theta=\pi$, and then doubling the result to allow for the equal contribution of magnetic field energy

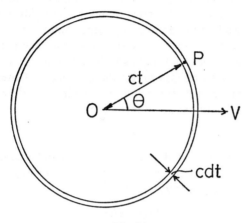

Fig. 21

and electric field energy characteristic of Maxwell's equations. This will give the energy radiated in the time interval dt. The result is:

$$2\int_0^\pi\left[\frac{1}{8\pi}(ef\sin\theta/c^3t)^2 2\pi(ct)^2\sin\theta\ cdt\right]d\theta=2e^2f^2dt/3c^3 \qquad (75)$$

At this stage we are not interested in what happens remote from the charge. We question the assumption that energy is radiated at all and concentrate attention on the source of the alleged radiation. This is where the accelerating field V does its work and interacts with the field set up by e itself. The field energy density must then include the interaction with V omitted from the derivation of the Larmor formula. The field given by (74) is then:

$$\frac{ef\sin\theta}{c^3t}-V\sin\theta \qquad (76)$$

Squaring this and restricting attention to the time-dependent components, we obtain:

$$(ef\sin\theta/c^3t)^2(1-2c^3tV/ef) \qquad (77)$$

It is then immediately evident that there is no energy radiation if the latter part of this expression is zero, that is, if:

$$Ve/f = e^2/2c^2(ct) \tag{78}$$

Since it is the basic hypothesis of this attempt to deduce $E = Mc^2$ that there is no radiation of energy, we must admit (78). To proceed, let us distinguish between an electric charge confined by a boundary of radius a and the empty space surrounding this charge boundary. Regard the field of the charge in this surrounding space as an integral system. On this basis we may expect the Coulomb self-energy of the electric charge in the field surrounding the charge to exhibit a single-valued mass property related to the energy:

$$E = e^2/2a \tag{79}$$

E is now energy associated with the charge e but located outside radius a. This is the energy corresponding with the expression Ve/f in (78) when ct is equal to a. Therefore:

$$Ve/f = E/c^2 \tag{80}$$

becomes the condition for no energy radiation across the radius bounding the charge. Ve/f then becomes the mass property associated with the Coulomb energy E. We have arrived at the anticipated result that $E = Mc^2$.

We must now consider the case in which the charge e is so distributed within the sphere of radius a that there is additional Coulomb energy within this sphere. We will adhere to the assumption that the self-energy of any charge exhibits a single-valued effect outside the spherical boundary confining that charge. In line with this the mutual interaction Coulomb energy of two spherical shell elements of the same body of charge will be deemed single-valued outside the outermost shell. It is, of course, zero within this shell.

In the case to be considered we regard the whole body of charge in uniform acceleration f. Thus a whole succession of shells of charge de_x of thickness dx at radius x undergo acceleration at the rate f simultaneously. It may then be shown, by tracing through the above analysis and developing a formula such as (75) based upon (76) rather than (74), that the energy radiated in time dt is given by:

$$(4f^2/3c^2)[\sum de_x(\sum de_x/2c^2 - Vct/f)] \tag{81}$$

where the value of ct is equal to the higher x value for any cross-product component term involving $de_x de_x$. The reason for this is evident if we write the two terms as de_x and de_y, where y is greater than x. For $(de_x)^2$ there is no radiation from the radius $ct = x$, the actual radius of the charge de_x. Similarly for $(de_y)^2$ there is no radiation of energy from the radius $ct = y$. For $(de_x)(de_y)$ there is no energy within the radius y and we can only look for radiation from the radius y, but as we say there is none then the condition that (81) is zero is that the value of $ct = y$ applies to cross-product terms at the higher charge radius.

For each such component interaction it is then evident that the identity:

$$\frac{(de_y)\sum(de_x)}{2c^2} = \frac{(de_y)Vy}{f} \tag{82}$$

with y greater than x applies and may be written in the form:

$$\frac{(de_y)\sum(de_x)}{2y} = \frac{V(de_y)c^2}{f} \tag{83}$$

Bearing in mind that all charge interactions are counted twice in a summation, the left-hand side of the above expression is the Coulomb interaction energy component dE. Summing this for the total charge e gives:

$$E = (Ve/f)c^2 \tag{84}$$

This is the same as (80) but it now applies generally to any spherically-symmetrical charge distribution confined within a bounding sphere. It tells us that such a body of charge will, when subject to the field of other charge, be bound to move with an acceleration f if it is to avoid dispersing its energy by radiation. Thus we have deduced the property of inertia. By denoting Ve/f as the mass M we obtain:

$$E = Mc^2 \tag{85}$$

By the above analysis it is seen that there is a very good case for developing the $E = Mc^2$ formula based on the assumption that energy is not radiated. The flaw in the Larmor formulation has been discovered. It did not take account of the effects in the near vicinity of the charge due to the interaction of the applied accelerating field. However, all we have shown is that no energy emerges from a discrete charge when accelerated. This does not mean that the collective actions of many charges and the propagation of electromagnetic waves by accelerated charges play no role in energy transfer. Nevertheless one does need to be cautious about the assumptions in conventional field theory that energy is radiated, bearing in mind the scope for energy fluctuations within the sea of energy which appears to pervade space.

The essential point made in the above analysis is that the mass property is related exclusively to the intrinsic Coulomb energy of the discrete charge. This raises the question of how this energy is augmented when the charge is accelerated to increase the mass. Is the charge compacted into a smaller volume? Alternatively, are we to expect perhaps the creation of charge pairs in some quantum statistical manner? At least from the analysis in Chapter 2 we know that we need not look also for separate explanation of magnetic energy. This is a reacting kinetic energy and so must be a Coulomb energy associated with reacting charge.

Charge Equivalence

It is important to note that the derivation of the $E = Mc^2$ formula developed above involves a parameter c which is not the assumed electromagnetic propagation speed, but rather the speed at which an electric field disturbance propagates from an electric charge. This distinction commands attention because the parameter c for electric disturbance could well be more fundamental than that for electromagnetic disturbance. This leads us to consider the problem of charge equivalence, that is the identity of electric charge and that in evidence in electromagnetic actions.

First we consider the Principle of Equivalence given such great attention in Einstein's theory. This is the identity of inertial and gravitational mass. This is one of the earliest known facts of experimental physics. Galileo's legendary experiment at the leaning tower of Pisa and the later experiment in 1891 by Eotvos confirmed this equivalence. Further experiments by Dicke* have checked the accuracy of this equivalence to less than one part in 10^{10}.

Einstein's theory elaborates on the theme of equivalence of inertial and gravitational acceleration but it takes us no nearer to an understanding of the physical basis of the constant of gravitation G. Nor is there anything particularly surprising about the discovery that the mass which we know from inertia happens to be the mass developing

* R. H. Dicke, *Scientific American*, **205**, 84 (1961).

the gravitational effect. It obviously suggests that some inertial effect associated with a mass element produces the local distortion of the field medium, which in turn results in the gravitational attraction.

The equivalence of electric and magnetic charge is taken for granted in Einstein's physics. It is not wrapped up in a mystical 'principle'. Yet it is equally significant. An inertial mass M has a gravitational property we may express as $G^{\frac{1}{2}}M$. An electric charge e has a magnetic property we may express as e/c. There is the basic experiment by Rowland (1875) by which the magnetic action of moving electric charge could be related to current. Rowland's experiment was just as important as that of Galileo or Eotvos. Miller* in an article entitled 'Rowland's Physics' has discussed the importance of the experiment in confirming Maxwell's use of c in his theory, which was, of course, based upon the principle of charge equivalence.

The curious feature of this comparison is that c is basic to relativity, but the principles embodied in relativity are silent on the subject of charge equivalence. The development of magnetic theory has been less silent on the correlation of G with electric charge. It is interesting to trace the history of the Schuster–Wilson hypothesis,† according to which mass does exhibit a magnetic field as if it has an electric charge $G^{\frac{1}{2}}M$.

The derivation of $E = Mc^2$ by Einstein stems, as we have seen, from the use of c by Maxwell in his electromagnetic theory. Why electric charge and its magnetic equivalent are related by c is not explained.

In the new derivation of $E = Mc^2$ presented above, c was introduced as the speed at which electric field disturbances propagate from the charge exhibiting mass. This is the only speed that we can look to to account for the propagation of the Coulomb interaction between two charges via their field systems. It was in this way that the parameter c used in Fig. 17 was introduced to give an indirect connection with electromagnetic effects. Thus c becomes also the ratio of electrostatic charge and electromagnetic charge, that is the parameter used in Maxwell's Equations.

In concluding this chapter, it is noted that the J. J. Thomson formula for the electric inertia of the electron, $2e^2/3a$, as mentioned earlier in a 1904 quotation, is confirmed as a true mass formula, but for other reasons. The charge here is in electromagnetic units.

* J. D. Miller, *Physics Today*, **29**, 39 (1976).
† See H. Aspden, *Modern Aether Science*, Sabberton, pp. 28 *et seq.*, 1972.

Were e stated in electrostatic units then this formula would give Mc^2 as it applies to the electron. Thomson's derivation was based upon the integration of magnetic field energy throughout the space surrounding the charge sphere of radius a. This seems inappropriate, bearing in mind that we regard in this work the magnetic reaction as attributable to other discrete charge and the magnetic field concept is unlikely to have meaning over the microscopic range so close to the charge e. On the Coulomb energy explanation, note that the field energy outside radius a is $\frac{1}{2}e^2/a$ and, for uniform field intensity within the sphere, the field energy within the radius a is the volume $4\pi a^3/3$ times $(e/a^2)^2/8\pi$, or $e^2/6a$. The total Coulomb energy is $2e^2/3a$, which we equate to Mc^2 to find the same mass as J. J. Thomson. This formula will be used extensively in the further analysis in this work.

5

Quantum Mechanics

Universal Time

In Chapter 3 the concept of time dilation as required by Einstein's theory was questioned. The experimental evidence supporting time dilation was challenged and this means that there is really no clear case favouring the idea that we age at different rates according to our relative state of motion. Alternative explanations for the apparent time changes are available and are consistent with the old-fashioned idea that time is universal and is shared by all in a harmonious manner. Indeed, one could say that we all sense the same time because we are part of a universal clock woven into the properties of space.

In 1932 Dirac delivered his Nobel prize lecture under the title 'The Theory of Electrons and Positrons' and made the statement:

> It is found that an electron which seems to us to be moving slowly, must actually have a very high frequency oscillatory motion of small amplitude superimposed on the regular motion which appears to us. As a result of this oscillatory motion, the velocity of the electron at any time equals the velocity of light. This is a prediction which cannot be directly verified by experiment, since the frequency is so high and its amplitude so small.

Similar proposals had been made earlier by both Einstein and Schroedinger. Einstein imagined the electron as belonging to a Galilean reference frame oscillating at a frequency determined from the electron rest mass energy and the Planck relationship, and being everywhere synchronous.

Thus, on the authority of great physicists such as Dirac, Schroedinger and Einstein, we are led, when examining the microcosmic world within the atom, to feel that matter is locked into a rhythmic motion. The quantum world of the atom is a world in which time appears to be universal.

Matter is linked by space or the so-called fields which permeate
space. If time is universal then it becomes a property of space itself,
owing to this role of space in providing the universal connection.
Therefore, time must be connected with something which moves in
space, because time without motion is meaningless. But space is
devoid of matter if we consider the vacuum state. Yet there is motion
in such space. The aether is then essential to provide the medium
having this time-setting motion. We can avoid it by specifying
formulae which reflect its properties, that is, we can avoid using the
word 'aether'. This was the course followed in developing wave
mechanics. Formulae, and notably the Schroedinger equation, were
developed and correlated with experimental facts. The underlying
physical system was not taken as a necessary foundation. It could not
be firm enough, bearing in mind the failure to detect the physical
aether as the absolute electromagnetic reference frame. But equations
need some kind of foundation if they are to portray reality, and the
aether, as a universal clock, can provide such foundation.

It needs little imagination then to realize that Dirac's words quoted
above plus the ideas of Einstein lead to a model of the aether which
carries matter universally in synchronous circular orbital oscillations
in balance with something in space in synchronous countermotion
at the relative speed of light, the frequency being $m_e c^2/h$. Here m_e
is electron mass, c is the speed of light and h is Planck's constant.

Furthermore, from what has been said, space devoid of matter
must also have such a state of motion. We need then to distinguish
between the various elements moving in space. In Chapter 3 we spoke
of the C-frame as the universal reference frame for electromagnetic
action when matter was not present. Thus the C-frame becomes a
primary candidate for the cyclic oscillation. The counterbalance is
provided by something we will term the G-frame, which moves everywhere in the same cyclic direction as the C-frame but which, being
in juxtaposition about a common inertial frame, is always moving
at a fixed speed relative to the C-frame. This system is portrayed
in Fig. 22.

The line grid represents the G-frame and the solid dots represent
elements of the C-frame. These latter elements will later be identified
as the q charges or lattice particles introduced in Chapter 2. The
G-frame will be identified as the charge continuum σ, also introduced
in Chapter 2 but will also comprise the gravitons introduced at the
end of Chapter 2. Note then that a relative velocity of light applies

for relative motion of the q charges and σ, giving u in (54) as c. Also note that at any moment all the elements of the undisturbed vacuum medium move parallel or anti-parallel.

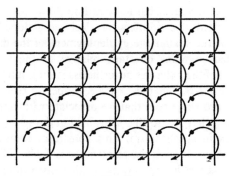

Fig. 22

When we come to consider the presence of matter, sharing the motion of the C-frame, then we will see justification for having a dynamic balance between the mass-energy of the gravitons and that of the matter plus the q charge system. The inertial mass of matter present thus becomes connected with the additional graviton mass, in exactly the manner required to explain the electrodynamic disturbance giving rise to gravitational effects. The equivalence of inertial mass and gravitational mass is inherent to such a model. Also, the mutually parallel motion of the gravitons and the continuum satisfies the requirement of the law of electrodynamics for direct mutual attraction along the line joining two electrodynamic disturbances. This gives the key connection with a gravitational law of force. It depends upon the interaction being insensitive to the high frequency of the oscillations. This is assured in the theory presented because the Neumann potential is proportional to $(\mathbf{v}.\mathbf{v}')$ and if $\mathbf{v}$ and $\mathbf{v}'$ are always parallel and equal then their product is a constant scalar quantity having no time dependence. The energy distribution throughout space as represented by the Neumann potential is then independent of the space oscillation frequency, provided the amplitudes of $\mathbf{v}$ and $\mathbf{v}'$ are constant. Thus the same forces are to be expected whether the frequency is very high or as small as we choose to make it. The gravitational potential must therefore be unaffected by the frequency and apply as if there is true instantaneous action at a distance. There is energy deployment when two gravitational disturbances, that is two particles of matter, move *relative* to the C-frame. Then we do have retardation effects as if gravitation is subject to a finite speed of propagation, but the key point is that the rapid cyclic motion portrayed in Fig. 22 has no retarding effect upon gravitational action. Nor, indeed, does it affect the electrical actions between the charges because the spatial energy deployment of the direct electric interaction fields remains constant relative to the C-frame. The circular motion of the q charges nevertheless is subject to the self-field action which gives the charges a mass property. However, it is a different mass property from that we associate with isolated charge in motion. The q charges are all constrained in the system depicted in Fig. 22 to stay in synchronism. This constraint comes from their electric interactions. It gives rise to extraneous fields which resist any distortion of this synchronous state. Radial distortions and lateral distortions can occur but not this frequency distortion. Therefore the q charges have only two degrees of freedom. This affects the mass property by causing any addition to the self-energy which we would normally associate with the kinetic energy of the charge to be dispersed throughout the q charge lattice. It is shared to the extent that any additional mass is distributed throughout the whole lattice. As a result there can be no relativistic increase in mass of a q charge. Its mass is effectively constant. Now this is very important, firstly because it facilitates analysis, but secondly because it assures that the system behaves as a linear oscillator and this is a key requirement to our understanding of wave mechanics. We can therefore use Newtonian mechanics to calculate the behaviour of the space medium, in spite of the fact that the relative velocity of the C-frame and G-frame is the speed of light.

Planck's Law

In Chapter 2 it was shown that the q charges when displaced in the continuum of charge density σ were subject to restoring forces proportional to the displacement. This can be set in balance with the centrifugal forces of the q charges, allowing us to write:

$$4\pi\sigma qx = m\Omega^2 r \qquad (86)$$

from (37). Here r is the radius of the orbits of the q charges and Ω is the angular frequency of space. m is the mass of the q charges.

x denotes the separation distance between the σ continuum and the q charge system. Thus $(x - r)$ is the orbital radius of the cyclic motion of the graviton and σ continuum system. The σ continuum and the gravitons are best regarded as an integral system statistically smeared into a uniform whole as far as interaction with the q system is concerned. Thus, since the gravitons are deemed to be relatively massive, they need only have a sparse population compared with the lattice particles having the q charge. Let m' denote the mass of the continuum-graviton system per lattice particle. Then:

$$m\Omega^2 r = m'\Omega^2(x - r) \tag{87}$$

The kinetic energy density of these C and G frame constituents of space is proportional to:

$$mr^2 + m'(x - r)^2 \tag{88}$$

because the space frequency is constant. We may then expect the electric potential energy of such a system to have minimized, so determining x, and the rest mass energy of m and m' to have been deployed between m and m' to maximize (88), inasmuch as kinetic energy is drawn from a source of potential energy and, with energy conservation, minimization of the latter means maximization of the former.

Write M as $m + m'$ to obtain from (87):

$$x - r = (m/M)x \text{ and } r = (m'/M)x \tag{89}$$

Put these in (88) to obtain:

$$(mM^2 - Mm^2)x^2/M^2 \tag{90}$$

Since M and x are constant, we may now differentiate this energy expression with respect to m to find its maximum by equating the differential to zero. This gives:

$$1 - 2m/M = 0 \tag{91}$$

from which we deduce that $m = m'$ and, from (89), that $x = 2r$.

The C-frame and the G-frame describe orbits of equal radius r. As their relative velocity is c, they move at a speed $\frac{1}{2}c$ in orbit. As the space frequency is $m_e c^2/h$, the value of Ω is given by:

$$\Omega = 2\pi m_e c^2/h \tag{92}$$

The radius r is then known, because Ωr is $\frac{1}{2}c$. Thus:

$$r = h/4\pi m_e c \tag{93}$$

At this stage it is interesting to show the link with a basic principle of wave mechanics, Heisenberg's Principle of Uncertainty. An electron located in the C-frame is never at rest in the inertial frame. Its position is uncertain by an amount $2r$ and its momentum is uncertain owing to the constant reversal of its motion at speed $\frac{1}{2}c$. The uncertainty of momentum is twice its instantaneous momentum $\frac{1}{2}m_e c$. Thus the product of uncertainty of momentum and uncertainty of position is $2m_e cr$, which, according to the Heisenberg Principle, is $h/2\pi$. This is confirmed by (93).

Eddington[*] wrote in 1929 about the Heisenberg uncertainty principle and said:

A particle may have position or it may have velocity but it cannot in any exact sense have both.

In the sense of our analysis, a particle at rest in the electromagnetic reference frame of free space does have velocity in the inertial frame. In an exact sense it has velocity and position, but we must not think it is at rest when it is always moving, nor do we ever need to say exactly where it is in its motion about the inertial frame, because all matter shares the same motion and is *relatively* at rest in this respect.

Our analysis so far does tell us that an electron has an intrinsic motion when at rest in the electromagnetic reference frame. Its own angular momentum is $m_e cr/2$ but there is a connected angular momentum due to the balance afforded by the G-frame. Thus the total angular momentum intrinsic to the electron and due to the motion of the space medium is $m_e cr$, which, from (93) is $h/4\pi$. This is the well-known value associated with electron spin.

The universal motion at the angular velocity Ω defines a fixed direction in space. A direction anisotropy in the properties of space is not in evidence in experiments so far, though the space medium is interacting with high energy particles and upsetting the parities which apply theoretically. When we come to study the rotation of the space medium with the Earth, it will then be seen that the earth's magnetic moment indicates that the axes appropriate to Ω are approximately normal to the plane in which the planets move about the sun. It is

[*] A. S. Eddington, *The Nature of the Physical World*, Cambridge University Press, p. 220, 1929.

probable from this that the space motion at the angular velocity Ω, though the same throughout all space in magnitude, may be directed in different directions in the environment of different and widely spaced stellar bodies. There may be space domains measured in dimensions of many light years and within which Ω is unidirectional. Its direction may change from one domain to the next, affecting gravitational interaction between bodies located in separate domains. These are cosmological questions to be addressed in Chapter 8. Suffice it to say here that the direction of Ω is of no significance to the analysis in this and the next chapter. Space behaves as an isotropic medium in its quantum mechanical interactions with the atom.

An electromagnetic wave is a propagated disturbance of the lattice structure formed by the q charges. The lattice can be disturbed if a discrete non-spherical unit of it rotates and so sets up a radial pulsation. This is depicted in Fig. 23. A cubic unit is shown rotating about

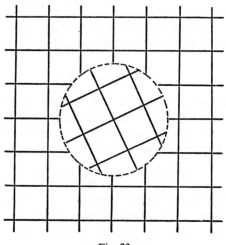

Fig. 23

a central axis. Any axis through the centre of the cubic unit can be chosen. The direction does not have to be parallel either with the direction of the Ω motion or a recognized direction of the lattice. The rotation will disturb the lattice at a frequency proportional to the speed of rotation of the unit. The three-dimensional symmetry assures that the unit has the same moment of inertia about any axis through its centre. The axis can be inclined to the lattice forming the unit. Therefore, the propagated disturbance frequency v will be directly related to the angular momentum of the unit and independent of the angular momentum vector. Our object is to show that this has meaning in relation to Planck's radiation law:

$$E = hv \qquad (94)$$

and the rotating cubic lattice will henceforth be termed the photon unit. Before showing how (94) is supported by this theoretical enquiry, a proof will be given for the above-asserted inertial properties.

The photon unit is considered as an array of lattice particles locked in fixed relative positions. Take co-ordinates referenced on the centre of the unit. Imagine a particle with co-ordinates x, y, z distant p from the origin. Take spin about the x axis. The moment of the particle about this axis is $y^2 + z^2$. This is $p^2 - x^2$. Now take spin about an axis inclined at an angle θ with the x axis. The moment about this new axis is $p^2\sin^2\theta$, or $p^2 - p^2\cos^2\theta$. Let l, m, n denote the direction cosines of this new axis of spin, relative to the x, y, z axes. Then the moment about the new axis found from the direction cosine formula for $\cos\theta$ is:

$$p^2 - (lx + my + nz)^2 \qquad (95)$$

If now we apply this to a group of particles having three-dimensional symmetry, there is a particle with co-ordinate $-x$ for every one with co-ordinate $+x$. Similarly for y and z. Thus cross-multiples of x, y and z cancel. The expression (95) then becomes a summation:

$$\sum p^2 - (l^2\sum x^2 + m^2\sum y^2 + n^2\sum z^2) \qquad (96)$$

Cubic symmetry means that it does not matter if x, y and z are interchanged. Consequently their summations must be equal. Then, since the sum of the squares of direction cosines is unity, we find the expression in (96) becomes the summation of $p^2 - x^2$ for all particles in the group. This is independent of the direction of spin.

A little consideration will show that if the photon unit depicted in Fig. 23 rotates at an angular speed $\Omega/4$ it will develop an electromagnetic pulsation at the frequency of the universal motion of the space medium. Under these conditions there is no electromagnetic wave propagation since a little local adjustment of the surrounding lattice can contain the disturbance. A photon unit rotating at the angular speed $\Omega/4$ will be termed a standard photon unit. It is a quantum of angular momentum which is characteristic of the space medium.

Now when an energy quantum E is added to the dynamic state of the space medium it will, as with any linear oscillator, be shared equally between the potential energy and the kinetic energy. With the constant angular frequency Ω, this means that $\frac{1}{2}E$ is added to the kinetic energy. That is:

$$\frac{1}{2}E = \frac{1}{2}H\Omega \qquad (97)$$

where H is the corresponding quantum of angular momentum. Thus, even though the energy E may become dispersed throughout the medium, it carries with it a related angular momentum given by:

$$H = E/\Omega \qquad (98)$$

The space medium is known to react critically to certain energy quanta related to the mass of the electron or positron at rest. It somehow permits the creation of electrons and positrons at these exact energy levels, as if there is some kind of resonance at the characteristic frequency of the space medium. It seems essential to connect this phenomenon with the standard photon unit, especially so in view of the clear connection evident from (92). The standard photon unit must be associated with this energy quantum $m_e c^2$. Thus, from (98), H is $m_e c^2/\Omega$, which, from (92), is:

$$H = h/2\pi \qquad (99)$$

The moment of inertia I of the photon unit is given by:

$$H = I(\Omega/4) \qquad (100)$$

which, from (99), gives:

$$I = 2h/\pi\Omega \qquad (101)$$

Taking now a photon unit rotating at a much lower angular speed ω, this is related to the frequency ν radiated by:

$$4\omega = 2\pi\nu \qquad (102)$$

The angular momentum of this unit is $I\omega$, which (101) and (102) show to be:

$$I\omega = h\nu/\Omega \qquad (103)$$

Then, from (98), since $I\omega$ is H:

$$E = h\nu \qquad (104)$$

which is Planck's radiation law.

Note that the kinetic energy of the photon units caused by their rotation has been ignored. This is because the lattice particles forming such units are still locked into their synchronous motion with the lattice generally. Their masses are held constant and the energy which would have constituted their kinetic energy due to the photon rotation is dispersed.

Also note that the photon unit need not be a rigid structure when rotating. When near positions in which it is in register with the surrounding lattice it will have the same basic structure and this will determine I. $I\omega$ will be constant throughout the rotation, but neither I or ω need stay constant at the intermediate positions.

The Schroedinger Equation

A photon unit rotates and so propagates disturbances at the frequency given by (102). If an electron is constrained by such a photon unit to describe orbits at this same frequency and can deploy itself in the field as a whole between such orbital phases, it could, collectively with other electrons, screen the photon radiation. Such an electron would have a kinetic energy W given by:

$$W = (\alpha H)\tfrac{1}{2}(2\pi v) \tag{105}$$

where αH denotes the orbital angular momentum of the electron.

This orbital angular momentum is the minor orbital quantity associated with the photon unit screening action. It is taken to be equal and opposite to that of the photon unit, as part of this conservative role. Putting αH equal to $I\omega$, we have from (103) and (105):

$$W = \pi h v^2/\Omega \tag{106}$$

From (92) this is:

$$W = \tfrac{1}{2}h^2 v^2/m_e c^2 \tag{107}$$

The electron will need to deploy into successive positions throughout the photon unit field in order to effectively screen the wave radiation caused by the rotation of the photon unit. Let p be a measure of the probability of finding the electron within a unit volume at radius x from the centre of radiation. Then a spherical shell of thickness dx at this radius x will, on average, contain $4\pi x^2 p\,dx$ of the electron charge. The radiation field of an electromagnetic disturbance diminishes in inverse linear proportion with x. Therefore, to screen such a field the local motion of the screening electron has not only to conform with the frequency but has to be matched in magnitude by the charge effect. This means that the expression:

$$(1/x^2) \int_0^x 4\pi x^2 p \, dx \tag{108}$$

has to be inversely proportional to x. This is a requirement that p is proportional to $1/x^2$, which means that it is proportional to A^2, where A is the wave amplitude at x.

The position of the electron in the photon unit field will then be governed by a wave equation and A^2 will give the probability of finding the electron at any position in the wave field.

The standard wave equation of frequency v is:

$$\Delta A + (4\pi^2 v^2/c^2)A = 0 \tag{109}$$

Eliminating v from (109) using (107) gives:

$$\Delta A + (8\pi^2 m_e/h^2)(E - V)A = 0 \tag{110}$$

if W is written as $E - V$, denoting the difference between the total energy E assigned to the electron and its potential energy V. This difference is the kinetic energy W.

Equation (110) is the Schroedinger equation. This is the basic equation of wave mechanics and much of the success of physical theory which may be termed 'non-classical' has resulted from the valid application of the equation. As is well known by students of quantum theory, it is possible to develop the theory of the electron structure of the atom by taking the Schroedinger equation as a starting point. However, particularly in respect of the quantitative priming of the energies of the discrete energy levels of the electrons, the classical Bohr theory of the atom has to be used in conjunction with wave mechanics for a complete understanding of the atom.

The weakness of the Bohr theory arose from the assumption that the orbital electrons had angular momentum in units of the quantum $h/2\pi$. It is, therefore, interesting to see that this quantum emerges as the angular momentum of the standard photon unit in the above theory. It is the natural angular momentum quantum arising from electron or positron annihilation. It may then seem reasonable to expect multiples of this angular momentum quantum to be characteristic of possible motion states of the electron when freed from its minor orbital motion with the slow photon unit. On such an assumption the Bohr theory could apply to the electron as it is in transit between different field positions at which it halts to react with such a photon unit.

In such a transit the kinetic energy of the electron will be as determined by Bohr theory. The electric field interaction energy applicable between the electron and the nucleus of the atom will apply as in Bohr theory but throughout the transits and the photon unit interactions. However, the kinetic energy as formulated from Bohr theory and that given by (105) apply to different states of motion. The energy must be the same throughout. This gives us a connection between (105) and the normal parameters of the atom.

According to Bohr's theory, an electron describing a circular orbit around a nucleus of charge Ze moves so that its centrifugal force $m_e v^2/R$ is in balance with the electrostatic force of attraction Ze^2/R^2. Here R is the distance of the electron from the relatively massive nucleus and v is the speed of the electron in orbit. By assuming that the angular momentum of the electron is quantized in units of $h/2\pi$ it is then possible to deduce that the kinetic energy of the electron is given by:

$$W = \tfrac{1}{2}mv^2 = 2\pi^2 Z^2 e^4 m_e/n^2 h^2 \tag{111}$$

where n is the number of units of the angular momentum quantum.

For the hydrogen atom with $Z=1$ and $n=1$, (111) becomes:

$$W = (2\pi e^2/hc)^2 m_e c^2/2 \tag{112}$$

Let us now calculate the angular momentum of the electron in its minor orbits when balancing a photon unit. This is αH from (105) or $I\omega$ from (103). Eliminating v from these two expressions gives us the angular momentum of:

$$(Wh/\pi\Omega)^{\frac{1}{2}} \tag{113}$$

From (92) this is:

$$(Wh^2/2\pi^2 m_e c^2)^{\frac{1}{2}} \tag{114}$$

From (112) this is:

$$(2\pi e^2/hc)(h/2\pi) \tag{115}$$

Since this is αH and H is $h/2\pi$, from (99), we find that α is given by:

$$\alpha = 2\pi e^2/hc \tag{116}$$

This quantity is known as the fine structure constant. It is a very important dimensionless constant. Its numerical derivation from a rigorous analysis of the structured lattice of the space medium is basic to the theory in this work. The discovery in the latter part of

1955 that this quantity could be derived from the geometry of the synchronous lattice system of Fig. 22 was the starting point for the research into the derivation of a whole series of fundamental constants, which are considered in the pages ahead. It will be shown how α is derived in the next chapter. First, however, since the calculation of the anomalous magnetic moment of the electron is generally regarded as the major example of numerical verification of theory and this depends closely upon α, it is appropriate to discuss this in relation to the author's methods.

The Electron g-factor

The theory of quantum electrodynamics by which the anomalous angular momentum properties of the electron in spin has been explained is a very complex theory, albeit one which has also proved very successful. Its methods differ from the more direct approach which will here be adopted. Our object is to show that a simple approach may well be as good and possibly better. Research into fundamental physics may not necessarily depend upon the use of relativistic or quantum electrodynamic techniques based on abstract concepts. There is considerable scope for simplifying quantum electrodynamics, having an eye upon the synchronous lattice model of the space medium shown in Fig. 22.

When an electron is in the confined state of motion we refer to as 'spin' it exhibits a magnetic moment which is not strictly e/m_ec times its angular momentum. The discrepancy is termed the g-factor. The ratio of magnetic moment to angular momentum is then g times e/m_ec. For the electron the experimental value of g is 1·00115965. The measurement of g is really by comparison with e/m_ec as it applies to an electron not in a state of spin. An electron in an atom may be in a state of spin in contrast with an electron moving freely.

One cannot really be sure whether the anomaly arises because there is something special about the spin motion or something special about the motion of an electron in a less-confined orbit. Nor, indeed can one be sure that it is the magnetic moment that is anomalous rather than the mass in one of the electron's two states.

To proceed, however, we will opt in favour of the mass property being anomalous. Thus imagine the electron charge as a seat of radial oscillations in its electric field. Suppose these oscillations occur at the speed c and at the natural frequency m_ec^2/h of the space medium.

There will be a radius from the electron at which a resonance can occur as these oscillations traverse the resonant radius in both directions in the period of one cycle of the natural frequency. The resonant radius distance will then simply be half of the Compton wavelength, or $h/2m_ec$. Beyond this radius, for a point charge electron, the electric field energy is $\frac{1}{2}e^2$ divided by the radius, or:

$$\delta E = e^2 m_e c/h \tag{117}$$

This tells us that the electron has a mass energy δE beyond a radius defining a resonance zone. From the $E = Mc^2$ formula this then means that it has a mass component δm_e outside this resonance zone, where:

$$\delta = e^2/hc \tag{118}$$

It needs little imagination to look to this mass to justify the anomaly. It is decoupled from the electron by virtue of the resonance boundary, at least notionally. If the electron moves along a path which is substantially linear compared with the scale set by the Compton wavelength then the mass δm_e must move with the electron. However, if the electron has a very restricted motion, confined well within the Compton range, as it has in sharing the motion in the space medium, an orbit of radius r given by (93), then one might expect its mass to exclude δm_e.

The consequence is that in the latter state, which we associate with spin, the value of $e/m_e c$ will be increased approximately by the factor δ. Note then that from (116) and (118) δ is $\alpha/2\pi$, and, as α is known to be 0·007297, this gives g as 1·00116. This seems to be a promising approach, having regard to the experimental value of g mentioned above.

Of course, it is a little difficult to imagine that the energy in the electron field can package itself into two separate segments in this way, but it may be that the mathematics tell us rather more than the physical picture on which the analysis is based. Some statistical processes are undoubtedly at work and give better basis for the mathematics than does the steady state model of the electron field.

One problem we need to address is the finite size of the electron on the basis of the J. J. Thomson formula. A point charge would have infinite energy on classical foundations. Yet, in the quantum world of space, it is difficult to be sure of any of our basic physical ideas. Some writers have speculated about the nature of space as a world of the sub-quantum, invoking the idea that neutrinos travel in all directions at high speed. We need not indulge in such speculation, except in suggesting that the sub-quantum world may in some respects be like a gas, setting the propagation speed for electric disturbances at the value c and providing the medium which asserts the resonant cavity properties we have just introduced.

In this it helps to think of corpuscles bombarding the electron and bouncing back to be reflected again by the cavity surface at the resonant radius. If these corpuscles are themselves electrical in character their path is likely to be ordered along radii from the electron rather than random, at least in the near vicinity of the electron. Beyond a critical radius from the charge surface their ordering will be random as in any gas. There is thus a probable transition between the random region with its three degrees of freedom and a region in the near vicinity of charge with one degree of freedom. This transition radius will correspond to an area three times larger than the area of the surface of the electron charge, in order that the pressure on the charge surface should equal one third that in the gas outside this transition radius.

The transition radius is therefore $3^{\frac{1}{2}}$ that of the electron charge radius a. The resonance occurs beyond this radius $3^{\frac{1}{2}}a$, so that we add half the Compton wavelength to the transition radius to obtain the radius of the resonant cavity as:

$$h/2m_ec + 3^{\frac{1}{2}}a \qquad (119)$$

This gives us a small correction term to allow for the finite size of the electron. The value of a is determined from the J. J. Thomson formula:

$$m_ec^2 = 2e^2/3a \qquad (120)$$

From (116) and (120), (119) becomes:

$$(1 + 2\alpha/3^{\frac{1}{2}}\pi)h/2m_ec \qquad (121)$$

The value of δ is then seen to be reduced by this factor $(1 + 2\alpha/3^{\frac{1}{2}}\pi)$ to become:

$$\delta = (\alpha/2\pi)/(1 + 2\alpha/3^{\frac{1}{2}}\pi) \qquad (122)$$

The g-factor for the spinning electron then becomes $1/(1 - \delta)$ or $1 + \delta + \delta^2 + \delta^3 \ldots$. From (122) this is:

$$g = 1 + (\alpha/2\pi) + (\tfrac{1}{4} - 3^{-\frac{1}{2}})(\alpha/\pi)^2 + (\tfrac{2}{3} - 3^{-\frac{1}{2}} + \tfrac{1}{8})(\alpha/\pi)^3 \ldots \qquad (123)$$

or $\qquad g = 1 + (\alpha/2\pi) - 0{\cdot}32735(\alpha/\pi)^2 + 0{\cdot}21(\alpha/\pi)^3 \ldots \qquad (124)$

This compares with the quantum electrodynamic derivation of Sommerfield:*

$$g = 1 + (\alpha/2\pi) - 0.328(\alpha/\pi)^2 \ldots . \tag{125}$$

The formulae differ by a few parts in 10^9. Hence we see that there is scope for matching the results of quantum electrodynamics by considering electrons as charges of spherical form and complying with J. J. Thomson's classical formula.

Later, when we consider the creation of the muon, we will also address the muon g-factor and show that similar results are obtained.

Meanwhile, however, and before leaving the problem of the electron g-factor, it is appropriate to anticipate a result we will come to in Chapter 9. It will be suggested that a particle of mass m will, even in what we regard as its rest state, store a dynamic energy equal to φm, where φ is the local gravitational potential, due principally to the masses of the Earth and Sun. This energy, as a kind of kinetic energy, may be stored by the transient creation of electron-positron pairs, in which case the energy will be part of the system beyond the resonant radius of the cavity. Thus φm will be energy of mass $\varphi m/c^2$ adding to the linear mass of the electron but not the spin mass. Thus g is increased by φ/c^2.

At the Earth's surface φ/c^2 is $1.06 \ 10^{-8}$, which adds $0.84(\alpha/\pi)^3$ to the g-factor of (124). Upon evaluation, using a recent evaluation† of α^{-1} of $137.035963(15)$, (124) becomes, with this modification:

$$g = 1.001159657 \tag{126}$$

This compares with the measured value‡ of:

$$g = 1.0011596567(35) \tag{127}$$

* C. M. Sommerfield, *Physical Review*, **107**, 328 (1957).
† E. R. Williams and P. T. Olsen, *Phys. Rev. Lett.*, **42**, 1575 (1979).
‡ E. R. Cohen and B. N. Taylor, *Jour. Phys. & Chem. Ref. Data*, **2**, 663 (1973).

6

The Vacuum Particles

The Lattice Particles

The q charges are the particles defining the lattice structure of the space medium permeating the vacuum. As with the graviton and the electron, we assign these particles a radius b which relates their electric energy and their charge q:

$$E = 2q^2/3b \qquad (128)$$

These particles have the lowest energy quantum of all particles with the electron-sized charge e. It will be shown that q and e are the same, as we derive the fine structure constant. This least energy state is justified by the fact that the lattice structure of the undisturbed settled vacuum medium must be the ultimate in stability. Furthermore, as part of this hypothesis, we go further and declare that there must be equilibrium between these lattice particles and the surrounding medium. If the energy E is associated with a characteristic spherical volume of $4\pi b^3/3$, then this energy density must be shared by the surrounding medium. Thus, with d as the lattice dimension and d^3 as the volume occupied per lattice particle, we can say that the total energy per unit cell of volume d^3 is given by:

$$E_0 = (1/2\pi)q^2 d^3/b^4 \qquad (129)$$

This total energy E_0 is, on average, at rest in the inertial frame, though its nucleation by charge can involve motion and migration throughout the cell.

The effective mass of the lattice particle is not found by using the formula $E = Mc^2$. When E moves there is the effect of a hole in the energy density of the surrounding medium moving as well. This exactly balances the mass property of the lattice particle in respect of its intrinsic inertial action. However, note that the surrounding medium behaves as an incompressible substance. It is like a liquid when subjected to displacement by the motion of a spherical body. We know from the study of hydrodynamics that there is an apparent increase in mass when a sphere is accelerated through a liquid. The formula is:

$$m = 2\pi b^3 \rho / 3 \qquad (130)$$

where b is the radius of the sphere and ρ is the mass density of the medium.

Accepting that this analogy applies to the problem of the vacuum, our lattice particles will have a mass given by:

$$m = q^2 / 3bc^2 \qquad (131)$$

Here we have used a value of ρ in (130) obtained by dividing E_0/d^3 by c^2, using (129).

The E_0 medium is important, as we shall see later, but, so far as electric interactions are concerned, we can ignore it and proceed to calculate the geometrical form of the lattice structure and its dynamic behaviour.

The lattice particles mutually repel by their Coulomb interaction. As in the formation of crystal structures within matter, we may then expect some kind of cubic or hexagonal lattice to form. This is the minimum energy structure. The problem with this is that the inter-action energy is negative. Such an energy condition is possible in matter because the interaction energy terms are mere component terms amongst a whole complex of energy quantities. When we deal with the vacuum state we have to be far more cautious.

The author found that if minimum interaction energy conditions were applied to the space medium and negative interaction energy accepted, then the lattice particles would all be at rest at neutral positions in the charge continuum. There would be no motion. The vacuum would have no character able to relate to time. The exercise of analysing the structure would have been meaningless. Accordingly, the assumption was made that the lattice particles would form in a structure which involves the least possible electric interaction energy consistent with it being positive everywhere.

This meant that there had to be displacement of the lattice particles and motion of these particles to hold them centrifugally in their dis-placed positions. The kinetic energy then becomes a factor in the energy minimization process. The more the displacement, the greater the kinetic energy. The displacement giving zero electric interaction energy for each lattice particle and equal displacement is the optimum. This meant a simple cubic lattice structure, a structure least favoured in crystals. In its turn this also meant that the problem of analysis was eased.

It was shown in Chapter 5 that x in (86) was $2r$ and that Ω in (86) was $c/2r$. Thus (86) becomes:

$$mc^2 = 32\pi\sigma qr^2 \tag{132}$$

Since the space medium is electrically neutral:

$$q = \sigma d^3 \tag{133}$$

assuming that q is a point charge. A correction for this will be applied later. Then, from (132) and (133):

$$mc^2 = 32\pi(r/d)^2 q^2/d \tag{134}$$

The evaluation of r/d is the prime task at this stage. We know the value of r from (93) and by finding r/d we will be able to determine d and so a value of σ if q happens to be the same as the electron charge. The value of r/d is readily found, because it is set by the condition of zero electric interaction energy discussed above.

The equation of electric energy in the space medium, neglecting self-energy of any particles, is:

$$E = \sum\sum q^2/2x - \sum\int(q\sigma/x)dV + \int\int(\sigma^2/2x)dVdV \tag{135}$$

The factors 2 in the denominators are introduced because each interaction is counted twice in the summation or integration. The summations and integrations extend over the whole volume V of space. x now denotes the distance between charge in this general expression. The inter-particle lattice distance d is taken to be unity, as is the dielectric constant. Boundary conditions are of little consequence. Electric interaction energies, when reduced to local energy density terms, can in no way depend upon remote boundary conditions. The lattice configuration assumed need not hold as a rigid perfect lattice throughout space. It can be distorted, but we do expect the synchronous character of the lattice particle motion to hold over vast space domains.

Differentiation with respect to σ allows us to set σ so that E is a minimum. This minimum not only depends upon a condition almost exactly expressed by (135), but also depends upon the displacement between the q system and the σ system. The differentiation of (135) with equation to zero gives:

$$\sum\int(q\sigma/x)dV = \int\int(\sigma^2/x)dVdV \qquad (136)$$

From (135) and (136):

$$E = \sum\sum q^2/2x - \sum\int(q\sigma/2x)dV \qquad (137)$$

This is zero, according to our set condition. To proceed, we will evaluate:

$$\sum q^2/x - \int(q\sigma/x)dV \qquad (138)$$

as it would apply if the charge q were at the rest position. The calculation involves three stages.

Stage 1: The evaluation of $\sum q^2/x$ between one particle and the other particles.

Regarding d as unit distance, the co-ordinates of all surrounding particles in a cubic lattice are given by l, m, n, where l, m, n may have any value in the series $0, \pm 1, \pm 2, \pm 3$, etc., but the co-ordinate $0, 0, 0$ must be excluded. Consider successive concentric cubic shells of surrounding particles. The first shell has $3^3 - 1$ particles, the second $5^3 - 3^3$, the third $7^3 - 5^3$, etc. Any shell is formed by a combination of particles such that, if z is the order of the shell, at least one of the co-ordinates l, m, n is equal to z and this value is equal to or greater than that of either of the other two co-ordinates. On this basis it is a simple matter to evaluate $\sum q^2/x$ or $(q^2/d)\sum(l^2 + m^2 + n^2)$ as it applies to any shell. It is straightforward arithmetic to verify the following evaluations of this summation. S_z denotes the summation as applied to the z shell.

$$S_1 = 19\cdot10408$$
$$S_2 = 38\cdot08313$$
$$S_3 = 57\cdot12236$$
$$S_4 = 76\cdot16268$$
$$S_5 = 95\cdot20320$$

By way of example, S_2 is the sum of the terms:

$$\frac{6}{\sqrt{4}} + \frac{24}{\sqrt{5}} + \frac{24}{\sqrt{6}} + \frac{12}{\sqrt{8}} + \frac{24}{\sqrt{9}} + \frac{8}{\sqrt{12}}$$

Here, $6 + 24 + 24 + 12 + 24 + 8$ is equal to $5^3 - 3^3$.

Stage 2: The evaluation of components of $\int (q\sigma/x)dV$ corresponding to the quantities S_z.

The limits of a range of integration corresponding with the z shell lie between $\pm(z-\frac{1}{2})$, $\pm(z-\frac{1}{2})$, $\pm(z-\frac{1}{2})$ and $\pm(z+\frac{1}{2})$, $\pm(z+\frac{1}{2})$, $\pm(z+\frac{1}{2})$. An integral of $q\sigma/x$ over these limits is denoted $q\sigma d^2 I_z$. The expression I_z may be shown to be:

$$I_z = 24z \int_0^1 \sinh^{-1}(1+y^2)^{-\frac{1}{2}}dy$$

Upon integration:

$$I_z = 24z(\cosh^{-1} 2 - \pi/6)$$

Upon evaluation:

$$I_z = 19{\cdot}040619058z \tag{139}$$

Within the I_1 shell there is a component I_0 for which z in (139) is effectively $1/8$. Thus:

$$I_0 = 2{\cdot}380077382 \tag{140}$$

Stage 3: Correction for finite lattice particle size.

Equation (133) is not strictly true if we allow for the finite volume of the charge q. For analysis in stages 1 and 2 it was easier to define q so that it satisfies (133). In effect q was made $q + \sigma V'$, where V' denotes the volume of the q particle. Bearing in mind that the mutual repulsion in the σ continuum will assert an attractive effect on a void in σ, we find that this assumption holds rigorously when applied to displacement effects. The point charge assumption is, therefore, quite in order. One correction that is needed is for us to avoid including interaction energy developed *within* the particle volume. The correction term to be subtracted from I_0 is:

$$\int_0^b 4\pi\sigma qx\,dx \tag{141}$$

This is:

$$2\pi(b/d)^2(q^2/d) \tag{142}$$

From (131) and (134):

$$b/d = (d/r)^2/96\pi \tag{143}$$

Thus, in units of q^2/d, the correction, found from (142) and (143), is:

$$(d/r)^4/4608\pi \tag{144}$$

From the results of the above three stages of calculation, we can now complete the evaluation of (138). Combining the above results we would find that the energy in the rest position is negative. It is the displacement of the lattice particles through the distance $2r$ from the σ continuum that adds the balancing energy:

$$8\pi\sigma q r^2 \tag{145}$$

This is obtained from (38) in Chapter 2. In units of q^2/d it becomes:

$$8\pi(r/d)^2 \tag{146}$$

The value of E given by combining these results, on a per lattice particle basis, is:

$$E = 8\pi(r/d)^2 - I_0 + (d/r)^4/4608\pi - \sum I_z + \sum S_z \tag{147}$$

We now have an expression from which r/d can be evaluated by putting $E = 0$. The difference between the two summations in these expressions is readily calculated by comparing (139) with the table of values of S_z. The S terms are all slightly higher than the I terms, but the difference converges inversely as the cube of z. The difference terms, beginning with the difference between S_1 and I_1, are:

$$0\cdot06346 + 0\cdot00189 + 0\cdot00050 + 0\cdot00020 + 0\cdot00010 \ldots$$

To sum the series, we match this convergence to:

$$0\cdot01350 \left\{ \frac{1}{3^3} + \frac{1}{4^3} + \frac{1}{5^3} + \frac{1}{6^3} \ldots \right\}$$

or:

$$0\cdot00050 + 0\cdot00021 + 00011 + 0\cdot00006 \ldots$$

for terms from $z = 3$ onwards. This sums to $0\cdot00105$.

Collecting these figures, we obtain:

$$I_0 + \sum I_z - \sum S_z = 2\cdot3137 \tag{148}$$

Then from (147) we can establish that r/d is $0\cdot30288$.

Although it has been shown how r/d can be estimated by manual calculation, a value of the zero energy r/d value has been checked by computer in 1972 and found to be $0\cdot302874$. The author is indebted to Dr. D. M. Eagles and Dr. C. H. Burton of the then-named National Standards Laboratory in Australia for their initiative in performing these calculations. The results are reported in *Physics Letters*, **41A**, 423 (1972).

Now in the previous chapter we derived the electron g-factor by discovering that there is a resonant cavity in the electron field and this spherical cavity had a radius determined by half the Compton wavelength or, from (93), $2\pi r$. Since we now have an estimate of r/d we can relate the lattice dimension d with this resonant radius. The electron resonant cavity is found to have a radius of $1\cdot903d$. This is drawn in Fig. 24 in relation to the space lattice.

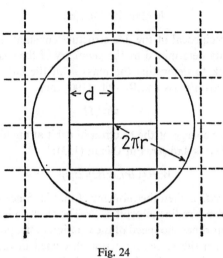

Fig. 24

It is seen that the electron resonant cavity will contain a $3 \times 3 \times 3$ lattice particle array if symmetrically positioned in relation to the lattice.

In deriving the Schroedinger equation we considered an electron in dynamic association with a photon unit, the latter pictured as an array of lattice particles having three-dimensional symmetry. It is then evident that the photon unit could be the very simple unit formed by a $3 \times 3 \times 3$ array of lattice particles rotating about their central member.

From (101) the moment of inertia of the photon unit is:

$$I = 4hr/c\pi \qquad (149)$$

because Ω is $c/2r$. The moment of inertia of the $3 \times 3 \times 3$ lattice is $36md^2$, because there are twelve particles distant d from a central axis and twelve distant $\sqrt{2}\ d$. Therefore, equating these values of I:

$$36md^2 = 4hr/c\pi \qquad (150)$$

Eliminate m from (134) and (150):

$$h = 144\pi(r/d)(2\pi q^2/c) \tag{151}$$

We know r/d and so have found an expression for h in terms of q and c. The quantitative data seem correct when q is equal to the electron charge e. Therefore, now accepting this, we write (151) in the form:

$$hc/2\pi e^2 = 144\pi(r/d) \tag{152}$$

This is the reciprocal of the fine structure constant. It is a dimensionless quantity determined by the geometry of the space structure.

Next we seek to determine the mass m of the lattice particle in relation to electron mass m_e. Rewrite (106) thus:

$$W = \pi h v^2/\Omega \tag{153}$$

W is the kinetic energy of the electron in orbit at angular frequency $2\pi v$. From (93) h is $4\pi m_e c r$. Put this in (153):

$$W = \tfrac{1}{2}(2m_e c r/\Omega)(2\pi v)^2 \tag{154}$$

The term $2m_e c r/\Omega$ is then the moment of inertia. Since Ω is $c/2r$ this gives the electron a radius of orbit of $2r$. The electron has to describe its orbits at four times the speed of the rotation of the photon units in order to perform the screening action discussed in the chapter on wave mechanics. Its angular momentum balances that of the photon unit. Hence its moment of inertia must be one quarter of that of the photon unit. Thus $m_e(2r)^2$ is equal to $\tfrac{1}{4}(36md^2)$, giving:

$$m/m_e = 4(r/d)^2/9 \tag{155}$$

From the derived value of r/d we find that m is $0.0408\ m_e$. We will later see that there is experimental evidence supporting such a mass value for the q charges of the space lattice. It is related to the temperature of the cosmic background radiation.

The Virtual Electrons and Positrons

Although virtual electrons and positrons are an essential ingredient in the vacuum medium, they appear to have no direct electrical interaction with other charge, owing to their pairing. They are important energy quanta. When they are created they need space for their charges. Yet we have on two occasions in this work already spoken of the incompressibility of the medium surrounding such charge. The section on the graviton highlighted the need for an incompressible fluid. Early in this chapter we struck an analogy between the energy medium holding the lattice particles in equilibrium and the properties of an incompressible liquid. Therefore, we are committed to think in terms of the conservation of the space occupied when electrons and positrons are created. We have, indeed, three possible binding conditions:

(a) the conservation of energy
(b) the conservation of charge parity
(c) the conservation of space.

How then can we account for the creation of electrons and positrons unless there is a corresponding annihilation elsewhere? The answer to be applied to the vacuum medium is that there is a state of equilibrium asserted between the lattice particles and any virtual electrons or positrons in the system. This has an energy quantum fluctuation associated with it, which interacts in creating elementary particles of matter.

Take one single lattice particle. It has the dominant space volume $4\pi b^3/3$ and little energy, but a single charge e. The electron or positron is the next largest particle in volume. As far as space interactions between the lattice particle and the electron-positron scheme are concerned all other known particles are of negligible size. Thus, for conservation of space in energy exchanges between lattice particle and electron-positron creation, the ratio of the volumes occupied by these particles individually must be an integer. Furthermore, for conservation of charge parity, it must be an odd integer. Thus one lattice particle of charge e can convert into N electrons of charge $-e$ and $N+1$ positrons of charge e, assuming the lattice particle has a positive charge. $2N+1$ is an odd number. But we know that the radius of a charge is inversely proportional to its mass energy. This was the basis of (128). Hence m_e/m, given by (155), when halved and cubed, has to be an odd integer.

The halving is necessary because the mass m is the effective mass of the lattice particle owing to its motion in the incompressible medium. m is half of the equivalent mass energy given by the formula (128). The ratio of the volume occupied by the lattice particle and that occupied by the electron is then found to be approximately 1844·5 and this is not an odd integer.

Accordingly, since it must be an odd integer, we must recognize that the value of r/d is not at its strictly-zero electric interaction energy condition. Minimization of electric potential energy is the requirement, combined with a positive value. From (147) we see that r/d must be increased to the first value that will satisfy the odd integer requirement. The ratio m_e/m must, from (155), be reduced. Obviously, the odd integer is uniquely determined by the physical factors involved. It is 1843. Working backwards from (155) we then obtain:

$$r/d = (3/4)(8/1843)^{1/6} \qquad (156)$$

Putting this in (152) gives a rigorous formula for the fine structure constant. We obtain:

$$hc/2\pi e^2 = 108\pi(8/1843)^{1/6} \qquad (157)$$

This gives a value of 137·035915 for this quantity.*

The ability of the vacuum medium to generate energy fluctuations requiring and releasing the mass energy of about 1843 electrons and positrons will be seen to be very important when we consider the creation of the proton. It has direct implications in our quest to determine the mass of the graviton. First, let us evaluate the energy E_0 given by (129). From (143) E_0 becomes:

$$E_0 = (1/2\pi)(96\pi)^3(r/d)^6 q^2/b \qquad (158)$$

From (156) this is:

$$E_0 = (3/4\pi)(108\pi)^3(1/1843)E \qquad (159)$$

where E is the energy of the lattice particle given by (128). We have shown that this is $(1/1843)^{1/3}$ times the rest mass energy of the electron $m_e c^2$. Thus E_0 is readily found to be:

$$E_0 = 412·665816 \ m_e c^2 \qquad (160)$$

This happens to be very close to the energy of two muons, which are heavy electrons with a mass between 206 and 207 times that of the electron. Accordingly, it is tempting to suggest that the unit cell of the space medium comprises a pair of virtual muons in general migration and providing the equilibrium for the energy of the lattice particle.

* B. N. Taylor and E. R. Cohen, in a paper in the Proceedings of the Fifth International Conference on Atomic Masses and Fundamental Constants (AMCO-5), Paris, June 2–6, 1975, note that quantum electrodynamic data can be interpreted to give a value of 137·03592, correct to 0·8 parts per million. However, we must also take note of the more recent evaluation by Williams and Olsen of 137·035963(15) referenced at the end of Chapter 5.

In recent times heavy particle decay has come to be characterized by the emission of dimuons. Indeed the ratio hadrons to muon pairs produced in high energy collisions has become an important parameter in particle physics.

It occurred to the author that one way in which to discover the mass of the graviton would be to suppose that it was a heavy particle which could decay by producing energy quanta E_0 corresponding to a muon pair plus the quanta 1843 m_ec^2, with the residual energy forming hadrons. Thus, in a book published in 1966,* the author proposed that gravitons of energy g might decay into pairs of muons plus pairs of the 1843-quanta plus one or two hadrons. Apart from single graviton decay a double graviton decay suggested by collision seemed possible. The need to separate the hadron energy from the 1843-quanta suggests that the latter escape in pairs to assure momentum balance. Below a tabulation is given of the energy needed to create 1 or 2 muon pairs and 0, 1 or 2 1843-quantum pairs. The former require 412 electron energy units and the latter 3686. An exclusion rule was applied by which the number of muon pairs could not exceed the 1843-quantum pairs by more than one. This excludes the combination 2, 0 as well as 3, 1 and 4, 1, etc.

muon pairs	1843 pairs	energy deployed	hadron product	g energy
1	0	412	2(2326)	5064
1	1	4098	966	5064
2	1	4510	2(276)	5062
1	2	7784	2342	2(5063)
2	2	8196	2(966)	2(5064)

Bearing in mind that we contemplate a decay of either one or two gravitons, inspection of the first three columns of the table tells us that the energy g is likely to exceed 4510, with the fourth and fifth listed decays involving $2g$. The first decay would then leave a hadron energy greater than 4098. This seemed too high from 1966 data to correspond to a single hadron. Accordingly, a pair of hadrons was deemed to be formed of energy $\frac{1}{2}(g - 412)$. The second decay suggested that the hadron product would be a meson of much smaller

* H. Aspden, *The Theory of Gravitation*, 2nd ed., Sabberton, Southampton, p. 81 (1966).

mass. There were two candidates, a pion or a kaon. A fit was found by using the kaon of energy value 966 (this is the positive kaon of today of 493·7 Mev). There was a sigma hyperon of mass 2326 (1189 Mev) amongst the few well-known hadrons of the early 1960 period. When a pair of these were put into the first decay, the same g value emerged. Next, the fourth listed decay from two gravitons gave the other mass value of the sigma hyperon family 2342 (1197 Mev).

The author, therefore, felt that the pattern emerging gave evidence of the graviton in the region of 5063 electron mass units (2·587 Gev). This was particularly encouraging because, as we shall soon see, this is the value which gives us the constant of gravitation G.

Furthermore, it had not escaped the author's notice that there was an interesting correlation in the ratios of m/m_e and μ/g, where μ denotes the mass of the muon. This arose because the volume d^3 of the unit cell of the space lattice was about 5060 times that of the lattice particle. This correlation was exploited by the author in his 1966 work to give a theoretical account of the graviton mass, as being 5062·75 times that of the electron. We will see later how this graviton is created in high energy reactions and show that it has connection with the recent psi particle discoveries. First, let us explore a little further the data in the above table.

The third decay seemed relevant as affording enough energy to create two pions, which, in the early references to pion mass, were shown to have a higher value of 276 than that of 273 known today. The fifth decay seemed also relevant as applying to the creation of a pair of kaons.

Data of this kind appeared in tabulated form in the author's 1969 book *Physics without Einstein*. Also, in the author's 1975 book *Gravitation*, in Appendix III, there is an extension of the decay modes. For example, the second-listed decay in the above table can result in the creation of neutral kaons of mass 975 if the 1843-quanta escape only after becoming neutrons of mass 1838·6.

To show the relevance to the constant of gravitation, we now take the expression (54) for G and, by writing u as c and σ as e/d^3, this becomes:

$$G = (6\pi x^4 c^2/ed^3)^2 \qquad (161)$$

By writing $m_e c^2$ as $2e^2/3a$, we can rearrange (161) as:

$$G = (e/m_e)^2 (4\pi)^2 (x/d)^6 (x/a)^2 \qquad (162)$$

If gm_e denotes the mass of the graviton, then by the standard relationship between mass and size of a particle of charge e we know that x/a is $1/g$. x/d is found using b/d from (143) and a/b, which is $2m/m_e$ and known from (155). x/d is therefore $(1/g)(1/108\pi)$. From this (162) becomes:

$$G = (e/m_e)^2 (4\pi)^2 (1/108\pi)^6 (1/g)^8 \qquad (163)$$

The charge/mass ratio of the electron is $5 \cdot 273 \ 10^{17}$ esu/gm. We have seen that g is close to 5063. Hence G can be evaluated from (163). It is found to be $6 \cdot 67 \ 10^{-8}$ cgs units, in full accord with the measured value. Only one minor correction to (163) seems necessary. The value of σ is really higher by the factor $0 \cdot 0002$ than the formula e/d^3 indicates, owing to the finite size of the lattice particle. Thus the value of G given by (163) needs to be increased by the factor $0 \cdot 0004$.

The theory in its state as developed to 1966 therefore gave a very strong indication that the graviton constituent of the vacuum medium had the mass energy $2 \cdot 587$ Gev corresponding to this g value of 5063.

The H particles

If a charge e of energy P and radius x_1 has surface contact with an opposite charge $-e$ of energy Q and radius x_2 we have a neutral aggregation of total energy E given by:

$$E = P + Q - e^2/(x_1 + x_2) \qquad (164)$$

Again, using our basic classical energy formulae:

$$P = 2e^2/3x_1 \text{ and } Q = 2e^2/3x_2 \qquad (165)$$

we can put (164) in the form:

$$E = P + Q - \frac{3}{2} PQ/(P + Q) \qquad (166)$$

The author used this formula in the 1969 book *Physics without Einstein* to analyze nuclear binding energies, but it was not until five years later that the simple connection between (166) and the proton was realized. In collaboration with Dr. D. M. Eagles* the expression (166) was found to have a specific relationship between P and Q for E minimal and the higher of P and Q constant. This was:

$$Q/P = \left(\frac{3}{2}\right)^{\frac{1}{2}} - 1 \qquad (167)$$

* *Il Nuovo Cimento*, **30A**, 235 (1975).

When Q was assigned the value E_0 given by (160), P was found to be:

$$P/m_ec^2 = 1836 \cdot 15232 \tag{168}$$

This compared with the known proton-electron mass ratio of $1836 \cdot 15152(70)$, the (70) term signifying the probable error in the last two digits.

This encourages us to develop a theory for the proton from this result. The problem is to relate the phenomological basis of (168) with the creation of the energy quantum P. To proceed, let us look back to (166) and imagine that it could represent the merging of two virtual muons. The energy E would then equal E_0. P and Q could presumably have any value but if, for some reason, P was set equal to the energy of one virtual muon or $\frac{1}{2}E_0$ then (166) shows that Q would be E_0. The point is that the Q and P energies can be in a two to one ratio in the aggregation and yet the system appears as a whole to have simply the energy Q. A neutral system has the same overall energy as a charged component and yet contains another charged component of half the energy. This is a most useful formula by which to explore elementary particle physics.

A theme which we will term 'charge interaction stability' will be developed next. The energy formula $2e^2/3x$ applied to all basic charges can be differentiated to relate energy E_x and a change of volume V_x:

$$dV_x = -6\pi(x^4/e^2)dE_x \tag{169}$$

This was the basis on which we obtained (53) in formulating G.

If we have two such identical particles with the same x value, then they can exchange small amounts of energy whilst their combined volume will be conserved. Conservation of charge and space is assured in such an interaction and, apart from the very small second order energy requirements, the overall energy is conserved as well. It follows that there will be a mutual stability between particles belonging to the same family if they are in close proximity. It is logical, therefore, to expect that when a pair of muons combine in the near presence of similar systems they can have a transient stability by which one of the charges retains the single muon energy quantum. Then, from the foregoing argument, the other is thereby also held transiently stable at the double energy quantum E_0 of the whole aggregation.

In their turn such systems afford a measure of stability for E_0

energy quanta of particles in higher energy configurations. The formula (167) is applicable to a system which is energized by one of the 1843-quanta already discussed. As the energy P now set in excess of 1836·152 decays, the energy minimization process within the $P:Q$ system will encourage selective energy deployment between P and Q. This accelerates the progress of Q to its optimum value. When Q reaches the E_0 level its further decay is halted by the stabilizing effect of particles elsewhere in the environment having this E_0 value. This will retard decay of the system and cause the P energy to linger a little at the 1836·152 level before the system degenerates and goes into rapid decay, feeding its whole energy back into virtual electrons and positrons.

The overall result is that in such an energetic environment the creation of E_0 quanta will also lead to the creation of transient particles of charge of energy 1836·152 $m_e c^2$. The creation process has a kind of resonance condition, inasmuch as a slight tendency for a particular particle form to develop is accentuated by mutual stability effects. These proton-sized particles will be termed H particles. They are important constituents of matter and provide the source from which protons are formed. The proton will be discussed in the next chapter.

Formula (166) has interesting application to the particle forms emerging from high energy collisions between electrons and positrons. The psi particle discoveries reviewed by Drell[*] in 1975 are particularly important. Formula (166) can be applied to show why the psi particles are generated. This explanation has only recently been presented by the author in a scientific journal[†] and is hopefully an indication of the firm foundation of the author's theory.

Note that the minimum energy value given by (166) is:

$$E_{\min} = P - P(k^{\frac{1}{2}} - 1)^2 \tag{170}$$

where k is used in the energy expression e^2/kx applicable to a charge e of radius x. k has been taken to be $3/2$ in the above analysis. Now, given that P is the energy of the proton 938 Mev, then $E_{\min}$ will have a value determined by k. k has to be less than 2 because any higher value puts the charges in closer contact than their radii allow. The range $k = 1$ to $k = 2$ corresponds to a range of $E_{\min}$ from 938 Mev to 777 Mev and there happens experimentally to be only one meson

* S. D. Drell, *Scientific American*, **232**, 50 (1975).
† H. Aspden, *Speculations in Science and Technology*, **1**, 59 (1978).

between 938 Mev and 784 Mev. It is identified as K*(892). It is then gratifying to find that when the value of $k = 3/2$ is used in (170) we obtain 891 Mev. This implies that the particle K*(892) arises by the energy minimization process in a paired charge aggregation which includes the proton.

Above we spoke of 'charge interaction stability'. Now we will consider the 'pair creation stability' which we used to derive the 1843-quantum. We saw that the volume occupied by a lattice particle could be taken up by an odd number of electrons and positrons and that this interchange of states could govern the equilibrium between the lattice particles and electrons. When we consider high energy collisions in the presence of energy quanta which are nucleated by charge e and occupy specific volumes of space, then we can expect interactions regulated by such criteria. Thus the graviton energy quantum g could regulate the stability of other high energy particles.

A form of 'pair creation stability' which we will now consider involves particle annihilation at a position A immediately followed by particle creation at a different energy level. Elsewhere at position B there is the reverse process. Energy is exchanged between A and B to assure energy conservation. At both A and B there is charge and space conservation. However, our hypothesis requires pair annihilation at A followed by the creation of two identical pairs at A. Thus the new particles formed at A will have a volume half the size of the other particles. Since energy is inversely related to radius, this means that there can be equilibrium between energy quanta related by the factor $2^{1/3}$. Thus in a g quantum environment we would expect to find $g(2)^{1/3}$ particles once high energy conditions prevail. Also, since two g quanta of opposite polarity are offering their space to four $g(2)^{1/3}$ quanta, two of positive and two of negative polarity, we could expect some hybrids to form, such as one of $g(2)^{1/3}$ with one of opposite polarity of $g(2/3)^{1/3}$. The latter arises from an exchange of the three $g(2)^{1/3}$ quanta for a single quantum occupying the same space when an opposite pair of the higher energy quanta mutually annihilate.

The relevance of this to the psi particles is immediately apparent when we consider an electron and positron colliding at very high energy to provide the energy E in (166). The energy quanta $g(2)^{1/3}$, g and $g(2/3)^{1/3}$ are deemed to be present. They will assert a stabilizing influence on the P and Q quanta generated in the reactions. A very likely resonance condition is one for which E is at the minimum value given by (170) and P is $g(2)^{1/3}$. With $k = 3/2$ and $g = 2 \cdot 587$ Gev, the graviton energy deduced above, E_{min} is found to be $3 \cdot 095$ Gev, exactly the energy of the first-discovered psi particle.

This is most encouraging. Now let us look for the second most-likely resonance. Here we find E from (166) when P is $g(2)^{1/3}$ and Q is g. With g as $2 \cdot 587$ Gev this gives E as $3 \cdot 683$ Gev, corresponding to the second-reported psi particle. The experimental value finally presented was $3 \cdot 684$ Gev, in excellent accord with this theoretical account.

Finally, let us evaluate the energy of the other particle predicted above. With $g(2/3)^{1/3}$ and g as $2 \cdot 587$ Gev, we obtain $2 \cdot 260$ Gev. The discovery of such a particle of mass energy between $2 \cdot 250$ Gev and $2 \cdot 270$ Gev at Fermilab was announced in August, 1976.*

From the evident relevance of these data to the positive identification of the $2 \cdot 587$ Gev particle, it must be expected that experimental verification of the specific existence of the $2 \cdot 587$ Gev graviton is possible. At the time of writing this book there is conflicting evidence on this point. A very significant particle resonance was reported near $2 \cdot 60$ Gev early in 1977,† but searches made independently‡ have failed so far to give confirmation. Hopefully, the $2 \cdot 587$ Gev graviton will manifest itself more directly in such experiments in the future.

Meanwhile, some further confirmation of the psi particle theory above is forthcoming from data on the staged decay of the $3 \cdot 684$ Gev psi particle published since the author developed the theory.§ The particle has five radiative decay thresholds at 3551 ± 4, 3503 ± 4, 3455, 3414 ± 3 and 3340 Mev, respectively. We would expect that if the author is correct and the psi particle at $3 \cdot 684$ Gev is based upon a P-Q combination, with Q as $2 \cdot 587$ Gev and P as $(2)^{1/3}$ times this at $3 \cdot 259$ Gev then these decay thresholds should be indicated by a connected theory.

To proceed, note that our expectation of decay arrested at succeeding thresholds will involve either P or Q halting at resonant levels at which there is a stabilizing influence from more prevalent particle forms having standard energy quanta. The dimuon energy given by

* N. Calder, *The Key to the Universe*, BBC publication, p. 122 (1977).
† A. Apostolakis *et al.*, *Physics Letters*, **66B**, 185 (1977).
‡ G. W. van Apeldoorn *et al.*, *Physics Letters*, **72B**, 487 (1978).
§ W. Tanenbaum, *Physical Review D.*, **17**, 1731 (1978).

E_0 in (160) of 211 Mev is an example, as is the muon energy of 106 Mev. Also, decay might occur by shedding energy which creates miniature P-Q systems, referenced on such standard quanta.

Put $P = Q = 106$ Mev in (166) and we obtain 132 Mev. Thus if we take our theoretical energy for the psi particle of 3·683 Gev and suppose that its first decay involves release of a coupled muon pair we are left with an energy 3·551 Gev retained by our degraded P-Q system.

This is the first decay threshold. At this 3·551 Gev energy the P and Q constituents, having lost momentarily their stabilizing connection with standard particles in the environment, may oscillate over a wide range of correlated values, exchanging energy between P and Q. When either P or Q reaches a low or negligible value, such as that of the electron or positron, it may easily be separated to leave the other constituent charge in isolation at an energy close to the 3·551 Gev threshold. These in turn provide standard energy quanta influencing other P-Q systems in decay and eventually recombining with a free charge to reform a decaying P-Q system. Thus we may look for the next decay threshold by setting P at 3·551 Gev and Q at the muon energy 106 Mev. The value of E given by (166) becomes 3·503 Gev, exactly the second psi decay threshold.

By reiteration, with P as 3·503 Gev and Q as 106 Mev, we then obtain the next decay threshold from (166) as 3·455 Gev. This is exactly the third decay observed.

Alternatively, since Q could have been a dimuon at this stage, because 3·683 Gev less 3·455 Gev exceeds the dimuon energy quantum and energy released by decay could have created dimuon systems which assert a stabilizing interaction, we could put P as 3·503 Gev and Q as 211 Mev. (166) gives then an energy E of 3·415 Gev. This is the fourth decay threshold.

Still another alternative, is for the 3·551 Gev system, influenced by the near presence of muons in the miniature P-Q system formed with this decay, to generate and shed a pair of muons of total energy 211 Mev, thereby leaving an energy 3·340 Gev. This is exactly the fifth decay threshold.

The numerical correlation of the decay thresholds now tabulated in Mev below is quite persuasive, and considered alongside the simplicity of the model used it greatly strengthens the author's thesis that the 2·587 Gev graviton is a reality as an energy quantum characteristic of the vacuum medium.

Theory	Observation
3551	3551 ± 4
3503	3503 ± 4
3455	3455
3415	3414 ± 3
3340	3340

These theoretical results for the decay of the 3·684 Gev psi particle were published by the author in 1979.*

It is of interest to note that in an environment in which these psi particles are created, one might expect other related psi particle forms. The P-Q system of energy 3·683 Gev could oscillate at this energy, exchanging energy between P and Q, as we suggested for the 3·551 Gev system. Assume that it does this but halts at a Q value of 211 Mev, that is at the dimuon quantum E_0 of (160). Then, for energy E unchanged at 3·683 Gev, (166) requires P to become 3·772 Gev. This could set an energy threshold for another particle having this energy value.

The discovery of a psi particle having the energy 3·772 Gev was reported in 1977,† another helpful pointer in support of our analysis.

Finally, turning away from the graviton and psi particle topic, but remaining with the P-Q system, we might consider the merging of two protons, or rather a proton and an antiproton, to create a P-Q system of total energy twice 938 Mev or 1·876 Gev. Suppose it is unstable and oscillates as suggested before to a limit state in which Q is an electron and P has the energy 1·877 Gev. Then, imagine energy release as the system settles in its minimum state given by (170). We are left with an energy quantum of 1·782 Gev. This is close to the recently reported energy of another new particle named‡ the tau, of energy 1·785 Gev.

In this chapter we have analysed the lattice structure of the space medium, relying upon the J. J. Thomson formula for charge as a spherical particle having mass energy equal to its electric energy. This formula has been applied universally, but in particular to the q charges forming the lattice and the gravitons balancing the lattice. It has been applied to pairs of charges forming P-Q systems and has

* H. Aspden, *Lett. Nuovo Cimento*, **26**, 257 (1979).
† P. A. Rapidis *et al.*, *Physical Review Letters*, **37**, 526 (1977).
‡ M. Perl, *New Scientist*, **81**, 564 (1979).

helped us to develop strong evidence from the new discoveries in elementary particle physics supporting the concept of the graviton energy quantum of 2·587 Gev. Thus, we have been able to evaluate Newton's Constant of Gravitation G, further strengthening the unification of the forces of gravitation and electrodynamics presented in Chapters 1 and 2. Incidental, it seems, to all this, is the evaluation, from the geometry of the q charge lattice, of the fine structure constant, an evaluation which is good to one part in a million.

It is submitted that there is good foundation for advancing physical theory on the lines introduced so far in this work, and, in particular, for studying the particle theme, bearing also in mind the other incidental result that gave us the H particle mass as equal to the proton mass to within one part in two million. We need, however, to be mindful of the possibility that much of the analysis applies to static and possibly transient situations applicable during creation and annihilation processes. Thus, although it seems that an electron has a solid spherical form most of the time in its low speed state, we have to be open to more complex behaviour in intervening periods.

The task in the next chapter is to examine how the principles developed so far can be applied to particles of matter.

7

Particles of Matter

The Deuteron

The positron was discovered in 1932. It appeared in cosmic rays and is, of course, merely a particle exactly like the electron but with a positive charge e. Positrons are ejected from radio-active substances, which suggests their existence in the atomic nucleus. It has been found that a proton can lose a positive electron, or positron, and become a neutron. Also, a neutron can lose a negative electron and become a proton. This suggests that the proton and neutron must each contain an electron and a positron. Both must contain a heavy nucleon.

All this supposes, without excluding the possibility, that there are no inversions of polarity of the charge constituents or energy exchanges between them as they undergo these various transmutations. If we go on to consider the prospect of combining the neutron and the proton, we find that there is a suggestion in the scientific literature that they might be bound together by what is called an 'exchange interaction' arising because they are rapidly changing their identity. The idea is that they are exchanging electrons and positrons so that, according to a proposal by Fermi, the neutron and proton are really different quantum states of the same fundamental particle. Now this may be true, but there are other possibilities. If we know that these elementary particles are aggregations of electrons, positrons and some heavy particles, and we know the physical size of these particles from our energy relationship as used extensively in previous chapters, it is worth while examining what may flow from this knowledge. The result contains a double surprise, and is all the more gratifying because of its simplicity.

The deuteron, the nucleus of heavy hydrogen, is the particle formed when a proton and a neutron are bound together. By studying this first we are likely to learn something about both the proton and the neutron as well. Also we do have a useful starting point because we know the measured binding energy of the deuteron. Wapstra and Gore* have shown its value to be 2·22464(4) Mev. In an article by McKee on the 'Nature of the Deuteron'† it is described as a diffuse vacuous particle of radius 4·3 10⁻¹³ cm.

Quark theory suggests that particles comprise an aggregation of charge components called 'quarks'. Early ideas about quarks of fractional charge $e/3$ or $2e/3$ seem less in evidence today. Quark theory is advancing more on the basis of quarks with charge $+e$ or $-e$. Thus the H particles of our previous chapter together with electrons and positrons become the prime candidates for consideration as the basic building blocks for particles of matter, at least as far as atoms are concerned.

The deuteron must, therefore, comprise two H particles which account for its main mass and an odd number of electrons and positrons, at least one of which must separate the two H particles. Note that two H particles of opposite polarity in contact would have a very substantial binding energy. This energy of electric interaction would correspond to the negative energy term in (166) and, for $P = Q$, this is three quarters of the energy of either P or Q.

In proceeding, we will, as before, not suppose that the energy of a charge e of radius x is $2e^2/3x$. Instead, we use the general energy expression e^2/kx and see whether the value of k can be determined by comparison of theory and experiment.

The choice for the quark structure of the deuteron is presented in Fig. 25. Electric interactions are deemed to favour the in-line configuration. Also we must remember that all matter shares a motion with the space lattice and motion relative to the lattice can induce electrodynamic effects. This is a factor which may well be conducive to the in-line configuration, because the charge may prefer to lie strictly in line with the lines joining adjacent lattice particles.

It is convenient to evaluate mass quantities in terms of electron mass as a unit, though remember that we are really speaking in terms of energy. The H particle is assigned the mass M and the electron or positron the mass unity. The electron radius is denoted a, as before. Model A depicts two positive H particles separated by one electron. We ignore at this stage the small radius of the H particle and consider all interaction energies referenced on the unit

* A. H. Wapstra and N. B. Gore, *Nuclear Data Tables*, **A9**, 265 (1971).
† J. S. C. McKee, *Physics Bulletin*, **23**, 349 (1972).

spacing *a*. Thus the energy represented by model A is $2M + 1$ for the self-energies plus three interaction energy components. The latter are $e^2/2a$ for interaction between the H particles less two interactions each of e^2/a between the electron and an H particle. Since e^2/a is the

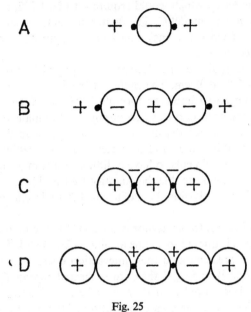

Fig. 25

unit *k*, this becomes $-1\cdot5k$. The total mass of model A is then $2M + 1 - 1\cdot5k$.

When this is repeated for the four models shown in Fig. 25 we obtain:

$$\text{A} \quad 2M + 1 - 1\cdot5k$$
$$\text{B} \quad 2M + 3 - 2\cdot317k$$
$$\text{C} \quad 2M + 3 - 2\cdot917k$$
$$\text{D} \quad 2M + 5 - 3\cdot558k$$

The deuteron will be the one having the most stable form, that is the one of smallest mass. This depends upon *k*. The negative term in the above list represents the energy binding the deuteron together. Experimentally, this is about 2·22 Mev or 4·35 electron mass units. Note that the rest mass energy of the electron is 0·5110 Mev. Thus each model satisfies a different value of *k*. For model A, *k* becomes 2·9. We know this is impossible because *k* cannot exceed 2, as we saw when discussing the psi particles. However, ignoring this, a value of 2·9 would make the mass of model C least amongst the four models listed. Model B, as a model determining k is ruled out on direct comparison with C, the latter having less total mass energy. Similarly, model D, which would require k to be 1·222, is ruled out in comparison with model C. The deuteron has to be structured as shown by C. Then k becomes 4·35/2·917 or approximately 1·5, as we established before.

The classical radius of the electron often quoted in physics books is $e^2/m_e c^2$ or 2·8 10^{-13} cm. The radius of the electron recognized in this work, and based upon the formula $2e^2/3m_e c^2$, is 1·88 10^{-13} cm. There are three such particles accounting for the main bulk of the deuteron model under discussion. It is a cigar-shaped object of length 6 times this radius and diameter twice this radius. It could well appear in experiments to have a diffuse radius midway between these values, at about double the quantity 1·88 10^{-13} cm. This seems in reasonable accord with the radius of 4·3 10^{-13} cm, quoted by McKee.

Of special interest to the author is the fact that the binding energy of the deuteron is quoted to so fine a value as 2·22464(4) Mev. When two charges e are separated their interaction energy depends upon their separation distance. If they are separated repeatedly and the same energy is required then they must be separated to a definite distance, unless we contemplate separation to the fiction of infinity. An uncertainty of 0·00004 Mev then implies separation with certainty to a distance beyond about 3 10^{-9} cm. This seems a very high distance to regulate the binding energies of a nucleus. It is very nearly the radius of the electron orbit of the unexcited Bohr hydrogen atom. It is well outside the range of electrons in heavier atoms.

To reconcile this with logically-based physics, we need to have a mechanism which limits the separation distance between the quarks when transmutations occur. The author believes that the distance $2r$ in the space theory presented is critical to such separation. Firstly, the σ continuum and the oppositely charged lattice system are separated by this distance. Thus it is a fundamental separation distance for charge of opposite polarity provided by Nature itself. Secondly, it happens to improve the agreement between theory and experiment if we make such an assumption. Note that the energy of interaction at the separation distance is $e^2/2r$ and this is simply $\alpha m_e c^2$, where α is the fine structure constant. $2r$ is about 3·86 10^{-11}

cm. This is well free of the electrons in Bohr orbits and yet well beyond the dimensions of the deuteron.

One question we face is how, upon separation, three positive charges from the deuteron dispose themselves in relation to the two negative charges. Here the author indulges in some speculation. We imagine that charges of the same polarity as the lattice particles actually displace these lattice particles and transiently assume their positions. The oppositely charged particles each take up positions in juxtaposition at the separation distance $2r$ and, further, the five particles interact with a sixth charge in the environment to assert their interactions as three pairs. The separated system is shown in Fig. 26.

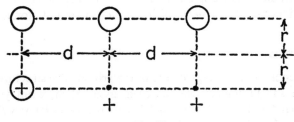

Fig. 26

The space metric has a cubic lattice dimension d, shown from the previous analysis to be about $6·37\ 10^{-11}$ cm. This follows because r is known from data put in (93) and we have established the value of r/d as $0·3029$.

The assumption we have made is that charge has an affinity for lattice positions and that three charge pairs in the critical disintegration ground state are arrayed side-by-side forming a rectangular lattice configuration of spacing d between charges of the same polarity and $2r$ between charges of opposite polarity. The mysterious sixth charge may be that of whatever influence caused the disintegration. It could have been a charged particle conveying the energy needed to trigger the disintegration.

The calculation of the total interaction energy for the system shown in Fig. 26 may be verified as giving:

$$-\alpha m_e c^2[3 - 5z + 4z(1 + z^2)^{-\frac{1}{2}} + z(1 + \tfrac{1}{4}z^2)^{-\frac{1}{2}}] \qquad (171)$$

Here z denotes $2r/d$. Note that α is $0·007298$. The value of (171) is $-0·01914\ m_e c^2$.

In the basic model C of the deuteron, assuming charge separation to infinity, the binding energy was 4·375 m_ec^2. This was subject to a reduction to allow for the finite size of the H particles. These are proton-sized and their effect is to reduce this calculated binding energy by a factor of 1/1836, that is to 4·37262 m_ec^2. Adjusting this for the ground state correction just calculated, that is subtracting 0·01914 m_ec^2, gives 4·35348 m_ec^2 as the theoretical energy needed to trigger disintegration of the deuteron. The conversion factor to Mev is 0·511003. Accordingly, the theoretical energy derived is 2·22464 Mev. This is exactly the measured binding energy of the deuteron.

The result must, therefore, encourage us to believe that this deuteron model is essentially correct and that the lattice structure of space does have a role in the disintegration criteria of atomic nuclei.

The Proton

We come next to the structure of the proton. The structure of the proton and its importance has been discussed in recent years by Feynman* writing in *Science* and Jacob† writing in *Physics Bulletin*. Feynman's article begins with the words:

> Protons are not fundamental particles but seem to be made of simpler elements called quarks. The evidence for this is given. But separated quarks have never been seen. A struggle to explain this paradox may be leading us to a clearer view of the precise laws of the proton's structure and other phenomena of high energy physics.

The three constituent quarks forming the proton have the same spin property as the electron. Their angular momentum quantum is $h/4\pi$.

A proton must then, on our model, comprise an H particle and an electron-positron pair or a negative H particle and two positrons. The latter can be shown to be slightly more stable than the former, by the method used to analyse the deuteron. However, given an H particle as a starting point, the creation of an electron-positron pair by deployment of some of its energy is so probable that the prevalent form of proton is sure to be the one depicted in Fig. 27.

In the theory developed in this work so far we have relied upon

* R. P. Feynman, *Science*, **183**, 601 (1974).
† M. Jacob, *Physics Bulletin*, p. 175, April, 1975.

three basic principles. These require conservation of energy, charge
parity and the space occupied by charge. In applying these principles
we have found that interactions are quite complex but involve a
primary interaction in which charge parity plus *either* energy *or*
space are conserved and an associated secondary scheme of interaction in which the residual conservation property is catered for.
Thus in psi particle creation our primary interaction involved energy
conservation, whereas in the lattice particle-electron equilibrium
interaction the primary concern was space conservation.

When we come to consider the production of the proton from an
H particle we look to energy and charge conservation as the primary

Fig. 27

interactions and look also to intrinsic stability of the resulting proton.
Having created a proton, we must have intrinsic conservation of
charge, space, and energy. Given N charge constituents, each of
charge $+e$ or $-e$, we know that N must be odd for the proton to
have an overall charge $+e$. Also, there will be N radius dimensions
governing the interaction energy and the total volume of space displaced by the proton as whole. If there is a perturbation tending to
change the intrinsic energy of an individual charge component then
its radius dimension must change. For total energy and total volume
to be conserved in such a situation N must exceed unity. It must be
3 or more. These two conditions determine two equations which
only have unique solution if two, and only two, radius parameters
are involved. The proton must comprise particles in two sizes. Hence
we see that the H particle must appear in association with pairs of
identical oppositely-charged particles to form a stable entity.
Electrons and positrons are the likely partners. The proton shown
in Fig. 27 is the one of least total energy, with $N = 3$.

The energy is, of course, exactly that supplied by the H particle.
Thus the proton-electron mass ratio is 1836·152, as found for the
newly-created H particle. Obviously, in sharing this energy to
create the electron-positron pair and then recovering some from the

interaction energy of the resulting proton, the H particle will, as a proton constituent, adopt a slightly smaller energy value itself.

Our problem now is one of verification. Two confirmations of the proton model just developed will be given. We will calculate the energy released in the process by which a neutron created by disintegration of a deuteron decays into the proton. This will afford a numerical check. Secondly, we will calculate the proton spin magnetic moment, as a further numerical check. The latter involves techniques which are at the forefront of the current state of development of this theory and which have not yet been fully interpreted. The calculation of proton spin magnetic moment is therefore left until later in this chapter, where it also fits well with the outcome of our analysis of the muon.

If the deuteron model and the proton model are compared it will be seen that the deuteron has two negative H particles and the proton has one positive H particle. For the deuteron to decay into a neutron and a proton the energy added to cause this disintegration must also somehow cause the H particle polarity to invert. This is depicted in Fig. 28. There must, therefore, either be a polarity inversion or an

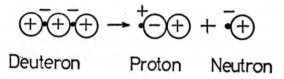

Deuteron   Proton   Neutron

Fig. 28

energy interchange between an H particle and a positron. Our attention must turn to this phenomenon before we can study the balance of energies in the deuteron disintegration.

Remember the process by which the 1843-quantum was explained. The characteristic volume of the lattice particle was utilized to create electrons and positrons and so account for an energy quantum of the same order as that of the H particle. Our hypothesis is that the H particle changes polarity by converting into a whole cluster of virtual electrons and positrons, mixing with an electron or positron of opposite polarity, and then condensing back into an H particle of opposite polarity to leave an electron or positron which also *appears* to have undergone polarity inversion in the process.

This is an interaction primarily involving energy and charge conservation, in spite of the apparent polarity inversion. We can expect the space requirements to be met transiently by the displacement of the space medium and the compaction of a lattice particle to form an electron or positron, coupled with an energy fluctuation elsewhere. Thus the lattice particle size could set the space quantum in which the electrons and positrons, possibly interspersed by some virtual muons, migrate at random, pending the formation of the new H particle. The self-energy of such a cluster, without regard to number or size of charges, is $3e^2/5b$, assuming that the charges are all paired with opposites except for one charge e. This is the energy of the cluster itself, taken as a uniformly-distributed spherical charge e of radius b, and not the self-energy of each charge.

This energy $3e^2/5b$ is the component which tends to disperse as kinetic energy. It is offset by a potential energy linked with the volume of the sphere of radius b. The sphere has an effective mass given by (130) and this involves an energy stored locally by the balancing graviton system. The energy is $e^2/3b$. The net result is that the inversion of an H particle involves a loss of energy given by:

$$E_{\mathrm{L}} = (\tfrac{3}{5} - \tfrac{1}{3})e^2/b \qquad (172)$$

Such a dispersal of energy must occur when lattice particles interact with the 1843-quanta of energy to create clusters of electrons and positrons in the mutual equilibrium process between electron and lattice particle. However, this is a universal activity and the energy dispersed is merely energy shared by the lattice particles. In short, the loss is reversible in the vacuum medium itself.

Evaluating E_{L} from our knowledge of the size of the lattice particle in relation to the electron, we find:

$$E_{\mathrm{L}} = 0.4 m_e c^2/(1843)^{1/3} \qquad (173)$$

or 0·032625 electron mass units.

It is important now to keep in mind that the protons produced by deuteron distintegration involve H particles which need not shed energy to form electron-positron pairs. There is enough energy or a source of electrons and positrons anyway. This applies to the onward stage of neutron decay as well. Thus such protons may be anomalous and have a slightly higher energy than the normal proton formed directly from H particles in isolation. The deuteron sourced protons could well have an onward decay stage which hitherto has not been detected or they may remain stable and exist in an anomalous form which has not yet been detected. The H particle in the deuteron is negative and is assigned the mass value M^-, with electron mass unity. The H particle produced from this by inversion is assigned the mass value M^+. Thus M^- is equal to $M^+ + E_L$.

The deuteron when excited to its ground state has used the energy causing disintegration to offset its interaction energy. The five constituent particles of total self mass $2M^- + 3$ then represent the energy in the ground state. They could reform to re-establish the deuteron but for the inversion of one M^- particle. This releases energy E_L which separates the particles well beyond their ground state level. Note that E_L is about 70% greater than the ground state excitation energy of the deuteron. Thus we can consider the constitution of the proton and the neutron as if we begin with the five particles at infinity.

The M^+ and the electron-positron pair come together to form a proton. In so doing they release their interaction energy E_P to augment the energy of the neutron. Thus:

$$(M^+ + M^- + 3) = (M^+ + 2 - E_P) + (M^- + 1 + E_P) \qquad (174)$$

The neutron lives for many minutes before decaying, an event which requires further H particle inversion with the positron being substituted by an electron. Thus:

$$(M^- + 1 + E_P) \text{ becomes } (M^+ + 1 + E_P + E_L) \qquad (175)$$

This divides into a proton to leave the electron with surplus energy:

$$(M^+ + 2 - E_P) \text{ plus (1) plus, as energy } (2E_P + E_L - 2) \qquad (176)$$

Some of the energy has been deployed into a captured electron-positron pair associated with the proton. The remaining energy carried away by the electron is $(2E_P + E_L - 2)$ and this is simply kinetic energy of the electron.

The value of $-E_P$ for the proton shown in Fig. 27 is the sum of three interaction energies. These are, approximately, $-e^2/a$, $-e^2/2a$ and $+e^2/3a$. The total is $-7e^2/6a$ or $-1 \cdot 75$ units of electron mass energy. The kinetic energy of the electron liberated by the neutron in creating the proton is therefore about $1 \cdot 5$ electron rest mass energy units, ignoring E_L.

The measured value is of this order and is known to be one part in 10^4. Accordingly, to check our theory we need rigorous analysis of the proton model, allowing for the finite size of the proton.

The formula for E_P is:

$$(3/2)[1/(1+n) - 1/(3+n) + 1/2] \qquad (177)$$

where n is $1/1836$. Upon evaluation this gives:

$$E_P = 1 \cdot 7492743$$

Thus: $\qquad 2E_P = 3 \cdot 4985486$

Add: $\qquad E_L = 0 \cdot 032625$

$$\overline{\qquad 3 \cdot 531173 \qquad}$$

Substracting 2 to cater for the creation of the electron and positron leaves an energy of *1·531173* as our calculated energy in electron rest mass units. It is the energy measured from the beta spectrum of neutron decay. The experimental value reported in 1976* is: *1·53116(8)*. This gives very good support for the theory presented.

The Pion

The technique by which we have just calculated the binding energy of the proton will now be used extensively to discover the process of creation of the pion and the real muon.

Our object is to calculate the masses of the pion and the muon to a very high order of accuracy and to check the results with measured values. The discovery on which this effort is based is summarized in Fig. 29.

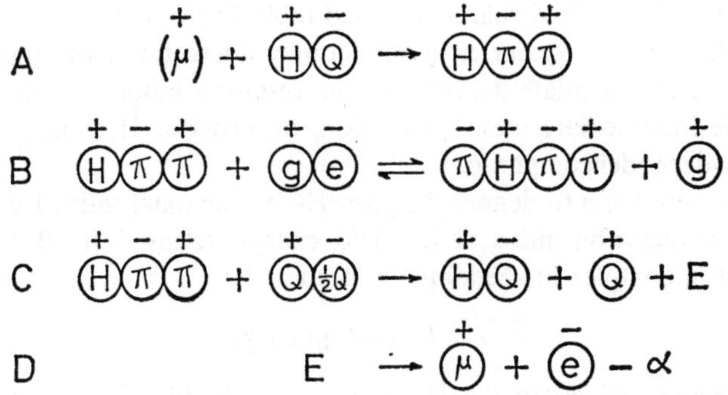

Fig. 29

* 'Particle Data Group', *Rev. Mod. Phys.*, **48**, S1–245 (1976).

The particle reactions are as follows:

(A) A virtual muon of positive charge combines with the system generating the H particles, Q being the energy E_0 of (160). Energy and charge are conserved to produce a particle aggregate similar to the proton but with the electron-positron pair replaced by a pair of mesons denoted π.

(B) The particle aggregate formed in A is able to convert a well-energized electron or positron, whichever has an opposite polarity to the H particle, into its own meson species, but as an addition to itself. Thus it can act as a catalyst in the type of equilibrium energy exchange shown in B. The graviton g has been chosen as the mediating particle because it happens to be around in the vacuum medium.

(C) The decay process of this catalyst occurs when an interaction with a neutral virtual muon combination, of the kind discussed following expression (168), occurs. This is an interaction with a surplus energy E.

(D) The energy E released by the decay of the catalyst is used to generate a real muon and either an electron or positron at the space system separation distance of $2r$, this accounting for the energy deficit of α electron mass energy units.

The latter condition was discussed when we studied the deuteron binding energy. The electron could merge with the Q^- particle to reconstitute the virtual muon combination in its neutral form, with a little energy release. The muon could decay into a virtual muon to reconstitute the virtual muon used in A. The whole cycle of events could, therefore, occur in a moderately energetic environment. It allows us to calculate the mass of the resulting muon and the mass of the intermediate meson, the pion, in terms of H, with a small-order dependence upon g.

We now use n to denote the pion/H-particle mass ratio. $1/g$ is the electron/graviton mass ratio. The energy released in B by the graviton complex in shedding an electron is:

$$1 - (3/2)g/(1+g) \tag{178}$$

The energy added to the H particle and double pion complex in acquiring the electron in pion form is:

$$nM\{1 - (3/4)[1/(1+n)] - (3/4)[1/(2+n)]\} \tag{179}$$

where M is the mass of the H particle in electron units as given by (168). By comparing (178) and (179) we should find equality. Therefore, given g we can evaluate n. An approximate answer of $n = 0.151$ is found ignoring g by equating (179) to zero. By rigorous solution, taking g as 5063, we find:

$$n = 0.1488809 \tag{180}$$

Now although we have spoken of the pion, we really have used the word 'pion' more in the sense of a quark, like the H particle. The pion, unlike the H particle, forms unstable particle aggregations. The stabilizing influence of other similar charged bodies in the local environment is not so strong in the case of the pion. Therefore, whereas the H particle, if created equally in positive and negative forms, has some kind of polarity bias favouring survival of the positive form (possibly due to the preponderance of electrons which capture the proton in a hydrogen atom form), the pion quark is just as likely to be present in positive as negative form during its short lifetime. The resulting pions always form in an environment populated by virtual electrons and positrons with ample energy present. Thus, they can capture both electrons and positrons in equal numbers and there is no special reason why the pion quark should deploy its energy to create an electron-positron pair. Instead, it can capture either two electrons or two positrons and form in the lowest energy state, as depicted in Fig. 30.

Fig. 30

The resulting pion mass for this state is given by:

$$nM + 2 - (9/4)[1/(1 + 1/nM)] \tag{181}$$

The expression involving brackets defines the three interaction energy terms in the pion system shown in Fig. 30.

From the fact that M is 1836.152 and the value of n derived in (180), we can evaluate the pion mass from (181). It gives:

$$273.1262$$

in electron mass units. This is in excellent accord with the experimental mass of the negative pion as given by Carter *et al.** Their value of $139,568 \cdot 6 \pm 2 \cdot 0$ kev is equivalent to $273 \cdot 1266 \pm 0 \cdot 0039$ electron mass units.

The Muon

The muon is a lepton. It does not involve any particle aggregation. It is a discrete charge like the electron. The pion quark has been evaluated from the energy balance of the reversible reaction shown in B in Fig. 29. Now we look to C to derive the energy quantum E by which the muon forms in D.

The Q systems have the same energy on both sides of the equation. They provide a basis for energy-free charge transfer. This arises from the use of equation (166).

The energy value of the $H:Q$ system is known from (170), with k as 3/2. It is:

$$M - M[(3/2)^{\frac{1}{3}} - 1]^2 \tag{182}$$

or
$$(1 - 0 \cdot 0505102)M \tag{183}$$

The energy of the H and pion quark system is given by:

$$\{1 + 2n - (3/2)[1/2] - (3/2)[1/(1+n)] + (3/2)[1/(3+n)]\}M$$

From (180) this is:
$$(1 \cdot 0626403)M \tag{184}$$

The value of E is then found by substracting (183) from (184):

$$0 \cdot 1131505 \, M \tag{185}$$

which, with M as $1836 \cdot 152$, becomes:

$$207 \cdot 7615 \tag{186}$$

Adding the fine structure constant $\alpha = 0 \cdot 007297$ and subtracting the unit mass of one electron, as required by the D reaction in Fig. 29, we obtain:

$$206 \cdot 7688 \tag{187}$$

The measured value of this muon mass quantity is:†

$$206 \cdot 76859(29) \tag{188}$$

---

* A. L. Carter *et al.*, *Phys. Rev. Lett.*, **37**, 1380 (1976).
† D. E. Casperson *et al.*, *Phys. Rev. Lett.*, **38**, 956 (1977).

At the end of Chapter 5 it was indicated that we would return to the problem of the muon g-factor. The above discussion by reference to reaction D in Fig. 29 shows that the muon and electron (or positron) are formed in close proximity. Indeed, the α term signifies that their Coulomb interaction energy upon creation is fixed for a separation distance of $2r$, the fundamental separation between the C-frame and the G-frame, the former being the frame we associate with the q charge lattice and the latter being the frame we associate with the oppositely-charged continuum and graviton system.

$2r$ is about one sixth of the Compton wavelength, the diameter of the resonant field cavity which we spoke of in explaining the electron g-factor. Accordingly, it is difficult to contend that both the muon and the electron (or positron) have separate field cavities at the time they are created. We suppose that when a particle pair is created at the $2r$ separation distance they share the same field cavity. Then the physical size of neither particle will be relevant as they both move around centrally within a common cavity. Accordingly, we take the cavity size as determined solely by resonance between the surface and the centre, making the diameter equal to the Compton wavelength. The formulae derived for the g-factors of each charge in the pair in this state should then be that applicable effectively to a point charge. The term involving 3 in (123) must be removed to obtain the relevant g-factor:

$$g = 1 + (\alpha/2\pi) + (\alpha/2\pi)^2 + (\alpha/2\pi)^3 \dots . \tag{189}$$

Imagine now the creation of an electron-positron pair from energy $2\,m_e c^2$. In fact, if created at the separation distance $2r$, the creation energy is $(2 - \alpha)m_e c^2$ but the balance of energy is needed to separate them fully. Assuming such full separation, the electron will adjust, upon leaving the sphere of the resonant cavity of the positron, and establish its normal cavity resonance. It adopts a g-factor given by (123) and has a stable existence at the resonant frequency of the space medium. The residual positron, however, is not so stable. Let us suppose that in such a transition the spin energies and field energy outside the resonant cavity are separately conserved. This is simple hypothesis, to be judged on the results obtained. In this case, the residual positron will be left with a contracted resonant cavity and a slightly higher frequency oscillation than that of the space medium. Also, its g-factor will be given by (123) with the 3 terms preceded by a minus sign. The g-factor will become twice that applicable for the point charge (189) less that applicable to the normal electron. Subtracting (124) from twice (189) we obtain:

$$g = 1 + (\alpha/2\pi) + 0 \cdot 82735(\alpha/\pi)^2 + 0 \cdot 04(\alpha/\pi)^3 \ldots \ldots \quad (190)$$

To this we must add the gravitational potential correction $0 \cdot 84(\alpha/\pi)^3$, as we did in deriving (126). The result is:

$$g = 1 \cdot 001165884 \quad (191)$$

It is then of interest to see that this compares with a reported experimental value* of the muon g-factor of:

$$g = 1 \cdot 001165895(27) \quad (192)$$

This is very close accord, but we have to explain why the residual positron in this electron creation process has the same g-factor as the residual muon accompanying the creation of a normal electron or positron. It will be understood that the above process could have produced a normal positron and a residual electron having this higher g-factor but being very unstable. Hence, we must examine the process by which reaction D in Fig. 29 could consolidate the residual energy around a muon with the same g-factor as given by (191).

The process we will suggest is based upon the electron-positron pair creation as a continuous sequence involving decay and recreation until eventually we are left with the muon.

First, note that the creation of a normal electron in the C-frame will be accompanied by the creation of a residual positron in the G-frame. Alternatively, there is the equal probability that we could create a normal positron in the C-frame and a residual electron in the G-frame. There is a minor difference because matter in the C-frame can have a different gravitational effect when compared with matter in the G-frame. As a result, a slight energy difference will exist between the normal electron or positron and the residual electron or positron. This is likely to be very small, possibly set by the factor φ/c^2 or $1 \cdot 06 \, 10^{-8}$ applicable from the gravitational potential at the Earth's surface, but it can be very important in explaining how the muon mass energy, which is not an integral multiple of electron-positron pair energy, can be constituted from an action cycle of the kind considered.

Next, suppose that the muon builds up from a residual positron as a normal electron is ejected, and that it absorbs all residual

* See data in Cohen and Taylor reference in footnote on page 102.

electrons and positrons that are formed. Also, any normal electrons and normal positrons mutually annihilate to feed energy back into the muon formation process, which only stops when all the energy has been used up. The hypothesis that spin and non-spin energies are separately conserved, as applied to the merging of the residual electrons and positrons, will endow the muon with a g-factor given by (191). Its resonant cavity radius will be much smaller than that of the electron and its resonant frequency very much higher than that of the space medium. However, albeit with recourse to hypothesis, we have obtained extremely good quantitative results and this encourages further enquiry into the nature of these processes, guided by the theory here suggested.

The author has already drawn attention to the curious fact that the g-factor for the point charge given by (189) is almost identically the average of the measured g-factors of the electron and the muon.* The discrepancy appears to be the gravitational potential factor φ/c^2 or $1.06 \ 10^{-8}$.

Thus the average of the measured values given in (192) and (127) is:

$$g = 1.001162776 \tag{193}$$

Putting α^{-1} as 137.036 gives, in (189):

$$g = 1.001162760 \tag{194}$$

An increase in α by one part in a million will increase g by 1.16 parts in 10^9 and since α is known to this order of accuracy the last digit in (194) could only be increased by 1 on this account. Also, experimental error makes the last digit in (193) uncertain to about 3 in all probability. Hence there is a discrepancy suggesting that the mass in spin is less than that in normal motion by an anomalous factor a little over 1 in 10^8, suggesting the gravitational potential explanation.

The point charge concept seems, therefore, to play a role in the g-factor anomaly. The gravitational potential argument has support. Therefore, whatever view one has about conventional quantum electrodynamics as providing the true explanation of the anomalous g-factor, these issues bear consideration. Also, it is mentioned that in the author's paper just referenced, attention is drawn to the work of Sachs in explaining the Lamb shift by methods not relying upon conventional quantum electrodynamics. This is important because

* H. Aspden, *International Journal of Theoretical Physics*, **16**, 401 (1977).

the Lamb shift is usually taken along with the anomalous g-factor theory as the main support for quantum electrodynamic theory.

The theory, as so far developed, has not yielded an understanding of the intrinsic spin properties of particles, particularly their magnetic spin moments. In an earlier version of this work (the author's book *Physics without Einstein*) some progress in this regard was claimed. However, these early ideas do not warrant inclusion in this present work. A result which is worth mentioning is the newly-discovered technique for deriving the proton spin magnetic moment. Until similar methods can be applied to other particles this approach must be regarded as tentative. It is of special interest owing to the extremely accurate result obtained.

The gyromagnetic properties of a simple charge are known to be given by the formula:

$$\frac{(MM)}{(AM)} = \frac{e}{mc} \tag{195}$$

At the end of Chapter 2 we showed that this arose from a half-field reaction effect, as in normal theory we would expect the ratio of magnetic moment (MM) to angular momentum (AM) to be $e/2mc$, where e/m is the charge-mass ratio of the particle under study.

The half-field reaction will now be applied to a complex of protons and muons in which the protons are reacting to the muon fields in spin. Thus:

$$(AM) = (m_\mu c/e)(MM) - (m_p c/e)\tfrac{1}{2}(MM) \tag{196}$$

Here m_μ is the muon mass and m_p the proton mass. This gives the angular momentum of the complex per muon, it being the muon angular momentum $h/4\pi$ offset by that of the reacting proton system. Thus (196) can be written as:

$$(AM) = (h/4\pi)(1 - m_p/2m_\mu) \tag{197}$$

Now this is a non-integral angular momentum quantum. Ideally, it should be exactly balanced by something in counter-spin. Also, although we have spoken of a proton reacting in the muon complex, we may just as well have referred to H particles. The same formula (197) would follow because the H particles have the same mass as the proton. Looking then for a system to set in counter-spin, let us take the proton form as presented in Fig. 27. Divide the angular momentum between its H particle and the electron-positron pair in proportion to their masses. Then assume a slight separation so that the H particle spins about its own central axis x–x but the electron-positron pair reacts to an applied magnetic field and also spins in the manner shown in Fig. 31. The electron and positron rotate

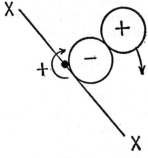

Fig. 31

together about the spin axis and this axis touches the innermost member of the pair.

The muon complex is not shown but it has shed angular momentum given by (197) to the system shown. The H particle in Fig. 31 asserts no magnetic moment. Its angular momentum has no contribution to the resonance state in spin. It may have its own spin angular momentum $h/4\pi$ in addition to that added by this interaction. The electron-positron charge pair will assert a magnetic moment related to the angular momentum added. This magnetic moment is moderated by a form factor f. The outermost charge contributes 3^2 times as much magnetic moment and angular momentum as the innermost, because it is at three times the radius. However, the charges are opposite in polarity. Thus their magnetic effects offset each other and their angular momenta add. f becomes $3^2 - 1$ divided by $3^2 + 1$, or 0·8. The magnetic moment of the charge pair is then 0·8 times $e/2m_e c$ times their combined angular momentum. The $2m_e$ factor is the mass of the electron plus positron. Their angular momentum is $2m_e/m_p$ times the expression given by (197). Therefore the measured spin magnetic moment should be:

$$(MM)_p = (eh/4\pi m_p c)(0·8)(m_p/2m_\mu - 1) \qquad (198)$$

The actual measurement of proton spin magnetic moment is based upon a frequency observation and referenced on the nuclear magneton $eh/4\pi m_p c$. Bearing in mind the result we obtained in expression (115), there is cause for wondering whether the basic angular momentum quantum of $h/4\pi$ assigned to fundamental particles is offset by the factor 2α in experiments referenced on atomic behaviour. Experimental data could, conceivably, have overestimated the spin magnetic moment of the proton by the factor $1/(1-2\alpha)$. If this were so, then, in nuclear magnetons (198) would need to be changed for comparison with experiment to become:

$$\frac{0\cdot8}{1-2\alpha}(m_p/2m_\mu - 1) \qquad (199)$$

This is such a simple formula, though its derivation is naturally unlikely to be accepted without considerable reservation. The point of interest is that we have found values for both α and m_μ/m_p in very accurate accord with experiment and so (199) should be determined with equal accuracy. With α^{-1} as $137\cdot0359$, m_p as $1836\cdot152$, m_μ as $206\cdot7689$ we obtain a value of (199) of $2\cdot792846$, which compares with an experimental value of $2\cdot7928456$. The last digit of the muon mass is critical to this agreement. Yet, in (193) we saw that the theory gave a figure of $206\cdot7688$ for this muon quantity. This is accord to within one part in two million.

Before leaving the subject of the muon, we will next deduce its lifetime. We find that this depends upon the migration of the virtual muons around the space cell. We also need to digress a little to discuss the nature of electric charge.

There is good reason for attributing a spherical form to electric charge. The difference between the positive and negative character of charge can be depicted as in Fig. 32. The arrows represent the directions of an electric field. Equally they could depict a state of

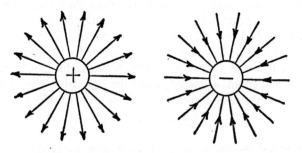

Fig. 32

motion. Presume, for example, that all charges of one polarity are expanding at any moment of time and all charges of opposite polarity are contracting. This is a workable hypothesis on the basis of the theory presented because the space medium has a universal frequency. If the charges are stable then there must be such a harmonic oscillation in their processes of expansion and contraction. Positive and negative then really signify a phase relationship, a difference of 180°.

The interaction between two charges of opposite polarity is then a mutual oscillation, depicted in Fig. 33 by imagining that the arrows reverse cyclically.

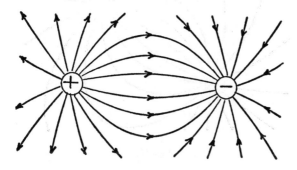

Fig. 33

We have noted that the size of the sphere containing the unit charge e is a measure of the energy of the particle. The number of flow lines radiating from a sphere is a measure of its charge. Beyond the resonant radius from each charge the field intensity in its interaction with the intensity of other fields determines the probability of energy quanta existing locally in the form of virtual electrons and positrons. These are themselves charge pairs as depicted in Fig. 33.

Imagine this pair of charges to become unstable, meaning that the contraction process fails to reverse in keeping with the phase of the oscillation. Then one charge will collapse to a point. The other will develop into a sphere of twice the normal volume, assuming that the interacting charges are of like size. This is illustrated in Fig. 34. The system is without character. The lines are devoid of meaning. They bear no arrows and do not symbolize motion. What has happened to the energy? Has the charge pair lost all its intrinsic character?

The residual spherical void will, by its volume, have some significance, provided we declare that the medium between the charge sphere is 'incompressible'. It retains the latent capacity to contract and, in so doing, it can nucleate a point source of motion elsewhere in the field. The point action is momentary only as the new charge is induced, its polarity being determined by the timing of its creation. Thus mutual annihilation of electron and positron means that they stop 'breathing' in and out, one ending in a point and the other in

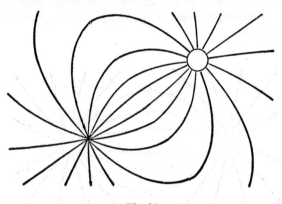

Fig. 34

an enlarged void. Their polarities are lost with this stoppage. However, the enlarged void is the seat of creation of a new electron or positron depending purely on the phase of the rebirth and the paired charge can appear from a point anywhere in the near vicinity. Thus these events of creation and annihilation can occur constantly as virtual pairs migrate all over the field. The real mystery is the nature of the energy quanta. The energy of the electron or positron is presumably the standard quantum. However, the smaller the residual voids associated with charge, the greater the energy quanta directly linked with charge. For our purposes, the energy formula $2e^2/3x$ used throughout this work need only be valid for charge in its stable state. Energy could be characteristically constant for any pair of charges and could be shared equally between them if they operate as 'virtual' pairs.

From this speculative exercise we are led to the proposition that space is permeated by charges which migrate at random by a process of annihilation and recreation proceeding at the natural oscillation frequency of the universe. A point charge arising from one of the two virtual systems, the electron-positron system or the muon system, can appear anywhere. A point charge from the electron-positron virtual field system will essentially develop into a stable charge for a short period anywhere in the field outside the resonant charge cavities. An electron point charge might appear anywhere, even inside another electron. We need, however, only consider the entry of the virtual muon into the charge of the real muon.

The line intensity within any charge sphere is uniform. This allows us to calculate the total energy. A charge of radius x has a field line intensity at its surface of e/x^2. This applies throughout its volume $4\pi x^3/3$. It corresponds to an energy term $e^2/6x$, which, when added to the energy outside the radius x of $e^2/2x$, gives $2e^2/3x$.

If a point charge e of opposite polarity appears within x at radius y then the energy becomes:

$$E' + e^2 y/x^2 - 4e^2/3x \qquad (200)$$

where E' is the energy of the point charge. To verify this note that the uniform energy density means that the base charge within a radius y is proportional to y^2. It asserts a steady force on a charge displaced from the centre outwards. Hence the term $e^2 y/x^2$. Also each shell of basic charge of unit thickness contains charge $2ey/x$ and so has an interaction energy $-2e^2/x$ with the point charge if central. To this we must add $2e^2/3x$ for the base charge alone to obtain the last term in (200).

We now imagine the condition for decay to be set by the above energy falling below a certain threshold. This is set at the energy zE, where E is the energy of the real muon. Thus (200) can be expressed as:

$$E' + (3/2)E(y/x) - 2E < zE \qquad (201)$$

The space frequency $m_e c^2/h$ or $1\cdot2356 \ 10^{20} \ s^{-1}$ is the migration frequency of the point charge muon pairs of energy $E' = \frac{1}{2}E_0$, where E_0 is given by (160). The value of E has been given in (193) in terms of $m_e c^2$. The volume of a sphere of radius y within which the point charge of the correct polarity must come to trigger decay is $(y/x)^3(m_e c^2/E)^3$ times the electron volume. In a unit space cell there are $(E_0/m_e c^2)(1843)^{4/3}$ electron volumes from the analysis leading to (160). From (160) this latter quantity is 9,324,644. Substituting E from (193) gives a lifetime T of:

$$T = \frac{(9{,}324{,}644)(206{\cdot}7688)^3 (x/y)^3}{1{\cdot}2356} 10^{-20} \text{ seconds} \qquad (202)$$

From (160) E' is $206{\cdot}3329 \, m_e c^2$ and this is $(1 - 0{\cdot}002108)E$. Therefore (201) becomes:

$$(3/2)(y/x) = (z + 1{\cdot}002108) \qquad (203)$$

If we simply wrote $(3/2)(y/x)$ as unity then (202) would give $T = 2{\cdot}25$ 10^{-6} seconds, which is close to the measured muon lifetime in its rest state.

If, however, we recognize the need to salvage the charge annihilated and say that an electron and positron are ejected in touching relationship, the value of zE is $1{\cdot}25 \, m_e c^2$. This follows from (166). Then z has the value $0{\cdot}0060453$. Then, using this in (203) and (202), we obtain:

$$T = 2{\cdot}1973 \, 10^{-6}\text{s}$$

The observed value* is $2{\cdot}197134 \pm 0{\cdot}000077 \, 10^{-6}$s.

The decay can be depicted thus:

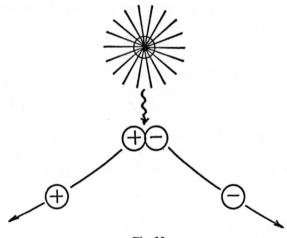

Fig. 35

Having given reason for the decay of the muon at rest, it becomes now feasible to explain how this decay is affected at high speeds.

In discussing Fig. 33 it was shown how the field interaction is always closed between two equal and opposite charges, regardless of their respective energies. These energies determine the individual

* *Review of Modern Physics*, **48**, 2, Part II, April, 1976.

stable-value radii x_1 and x_2 of two such charges, which collectively share a total energy E and a total space volume V given by:

$$E = (2e^2/3)(1/x_1 + 1/x_2) \tag{204}$$

$$V = (4\pi/3)(x_1^3 + x_2^3) \tag{205}$$

Now imagine a situation close to the fully degenerate state depicted in Fig. 34. One charge can thus exist transiently as a point charge if the oscillations remain in phase for a short period before the field energy needs to restore equilibrium. The basic character of the two interacting particles remains in the unique determination of x_1 and x_2 from (204) and (205), bearing in mind the constancy of E and V throughout this disturbance.

Take now the muon moving at speed and having x_1 determined by its total energy $\beta M_0 c^2$, where β denotes the expression $(1 - v^2/c^2)^{-\frac{1}{2}}$ of equation (65) in Chapter 4. With x_1 fixed it becomes possible to imagine that the muon in motion could exist in point charge form for short periods of association with other charge of opposite polarity encountered in its progress and regardless of the nature of such other charge. In the intervening periods the muon would have different form, its full spherical form of radius x_0, as determined by its rest-mass energy:

$$M_0 c^2 = 2e^2/3x_0 \tag{206}$$

In contrast: $\qquad \beta M_0 c^2 = 2e^2/3x_1 \tag{207}$

The hypothesis is that during these intervening periods the muon is in company with pairs of virtual muons, which account for the remainder of the energy. This is necessary, as will now be shown, because we need to conserve charge, energy and space throughout the successive quantum electrodynamic transitions of the muon when in motion. In Fig. 36 the muon is shown to change from state A to

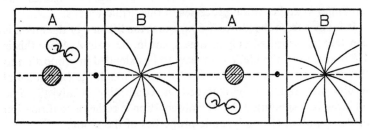

Fig. 36

state B and back again as it progresses from left to right. The trajectory of the muon is shown by the broken line.

In state A we have the basic muon of charge radius determined by its rest mass. It shares its total dynamic energy with virtual muon pairs of the same standard size. In transition from A to B the whole energy is carried by a single muon charge contracted now to the radius x_1. This transition is very short-lived. In state B the muon has gone into a degenerate form in association with a nearby charge of opposite polarity. Only the field lines from the point muon signify the locality of this nearby charge. The reverse process occurs in reverting back to state A, and so we have a constant alternation between states. Throughout, it is necessary to have a statistical conservation of energy, as between numerous muons in state A in any system at any moment of time. Also it is necessary to have a statistical conservation of space for each individual muon over periods including both states. This sets the further condition that state A will endure for $1/\beta$ of any time interval and state B for the remainder of that time interval. Note then that $1/\beta$ times the volume of the β muons of rest-mass size in state A gives the mean muon volume over a period of time as that of a single muon. Owing to the point charge character of the muon in periods of state B, the decay mechanism is restricted to the periods of state A. This results because y in (202) is effectively zero in state B. The decay in state A requires the migrant space charges to enter the basic muon. It is irrelevant if decay of one of the virtual muons is triggered, because these are in a constant state of annihilation and creation. The event would only trigger a transition back to state B. The muon would still exist. Note, however, that the virtual muons in a pair, if created at the separation distance of the C and G frames of the space medium, are much closer together than their distance from the basic muon, since they must lie outside the resonant field cavity radius. This precludes the muon from getting involved in the annihilation and creation processes of the virtual muons.

It follows from the above account that the lifetime of the muon is constant as measured only in time spent in the state A. Since this is $1/\beta$ of real time, the lifetime appears to be extended in proportion to the parameter β. This is what is observed, though the experimental results are traditionally regarded as confirming relativistic time dilation. It is submitted that the observation is rather a confirmation of the quantum electrodynamic properties of the muon.

The hypothetical picture of the step migration of a charged particle presented in Fig. 28 has a variant which should be mentioned. Suppose there is space conservation all the time, rather than on a mere statistical basis. Then, depending upon the energy of the particle, there will be voids having a volume equal to double an integral multiple of that of the particle at rest. For particle speeds up to $0.943c$, the speed at which the relativistic mass is three times the rest mass, there will be a single double-volume void as in state A in Fig. 36. However, whereas in Fig. 36 this void is occupied by a virtual charge pair, we regard this occupancy by charge to be governed by probability factors to assure that, on average, the energy of the base particle plus that of the charge-primed voids is equal to the energy of the charge in motion. To complete this alternative picture, we retain the point charge in state B to cater for migration of the particle, but the void, now three times the volume of the rest particle, migrates with the charge. Thus there is space and net charge conservation on a constant basis and energy conservation on a statistical basis. As applied to the muon, the lifetime dilation remains proportional to the energy.

This alternative quantum process avoids the idea that a stable charge may store energy by contraction and accepts that all charges, in their stable form, belong to families and have a standard unit size characteristic of a particular family. This may seem to invalidate the gravitation formula (54), but it does not, because the graviton together with its associated basic void displaces three times the usual $4\pi x^3/3$ volume of continuum. This means that (54) applies, but with dE equal to the whole energy quantum of the graviton.

As applied to the electrons in an atom, the migration of the point charges may well occur statistically without the voids following the track of the electron too closely. The virtual electron-positron pairs are induced in the field adjacent the electron and so may well manifest their presence indirectly rather than as a close coupling with the charge.

Quarks

We return now to the quantum characteristics of particles in high energy environments. The object is to examine possible processes by which fundamental components of elementary particles are produced.

There is some evidence, as we shall see by reference to quark theory, indicating the existence of positive and negative quarks which carry double the unit electron charge e. Multiple charge quanta can be imagined to exist, especially as the point charge migration of virtual electrons or muons requires charge to appear within the space occupied by charge of the same polarity. This presents unlimited scope for particle creation. Nature, no doubt admits a myriad of creation processes, but only shows us the very few which rely upon basic quantum probabilities and determine the existence of the most stable particle forms. Therefore, we will restrict attention to one single process involving the quantum cluster of 1843 electrons and positrons discussed when we derived the graviton mass empirically. Under natural circumstances, outside the accelerators of high energy particle physicists, it may be that this energy quantum of 1843 electron units (942 Mev) is the maximum energy fluctuation possible.

Let us see how it governs the creation of Nature's largest natural elementary particle. The process involved is one we will term 'half-synthesis'. Two particles A and B of opposite charges $+e$ and $-e$ come together from a relatively high separation distance and create a particle C of energy equal to A + B combined, in close paired relationship with one of half this energy. This process is readily understood from (166), with E as the combined energy of the two colliding particles. The particles of energy P and Q are formed and (166) shows that Q can adopt the value E and that if it does $P = \frac{1}{2}Q$. This possibility becomes a certainty in a high energy environment in which energy fluctuations involving continuous creation and decay occur constantly until a quasi-stable result is achieved. Energy fluctuations separating the Q and P particles, followed by recombination of opposite polarity P particles, regenerate the quantum $E = Q$. Indeed, such a system will synthesize particles of up to three times the magnitude of the energy fluctuations present. The actual particles produced depend upon the controls, in particular the energy quantum E_0 of (160), the 1843-quantum and the energy of the H particle.

To create Nature's largest natural particle we begin with the H particle of charge e and add an energy supplied by a particle of opposite charge. We may add an electron or a muon or a pion. Additionally we could add a neutral quantity, notably the energy E_0. Then we apply the process of half-synthesis by iteration until separation of charge would require energy fluctuations in excess of the 1843-quantum. The results are tabulated below. The various elements will be recognized from their numerical association. The H particle is 1836 electron mass units. The muon is 207. The pion 273. E_0 is 413. The electron is, of course, unity.

1836 + 1	1837	2756	4133
1836 + 207	2043	3065	4597
1836 + 273	2109	3164	4745
1836 + 413 + 1	2250	3375	5063
1836 + 413 + 207	2456	3684	5526
1836 + 413 + 273	2522	3783	—

The second column of figures gives the total initial energy in electron mass units. The third column gives the energy after the first iteration. The fourth column gives the energy after the second iteration. Since all the figures in the last column are greater than twice 1843 we cannot have any further particle synthesis. In the last example this precluded even the second iteration.

The data show that, on the assumption that the 1843-quantum has energy in excess of 1842 electron units (half 3684), the largest particle mass is 5526. On the other hand, if the energy associated with this quantum were really marginally less than this, the largest particle mass is exactly the value we found for the graviton, 5063. This mass gives the value of G exactly, when used in the gravitational formula presented in (163). It also gave excellent results for the psi particles. Hence it is reasonable to question whether 1843 signifies an energy quantum, or, at least, to question whether it accounts for the vacuum energy fluctuations. If, for example, the energy of the H particle were the governing energy fluctuation, then the 5526 value would have to be removed from the above table. The graviton would need then to be the 5063 quantum.

This puts in doubt the early empirical derivation of the graviton mass presented in Chapter 6 in relation to elementary particles produced by graviton decay. That derivation relied upon the 1843 energy quantum. However, this seems an appropriate judgement. The 5063 graviton quantum is supported by the derivation of G and the psi particle connection. Furthermore, the derivation in the above table also confirms this result exactly and is not critically dependent upon the energy fluctuation, provided it is less than 1842 and greater than 1688 (half 3375)

On reflection, the creation of 1843 electrons and positrons would not require 1843 electron mass energy units if they were produced in the near vicinity of one another. If, for example, each pair were produced together at a separation distance equal to the spacing of the G-frame and the C-frame, then the 1843 energy quantum would have to be offset by the factor $\frac{1}{2}\alpha$. This is analogous to the need to involve the fine structure constant in reaction D in Fig. 29. This reduces the 1843 energy quantum to 1836·3. This is just sufficient to create the H particle.

Reverting now to the multiple charge quark, let us make the bold speculation that charge can vary but that space and energy are conserved in a situation where the energy fluctuation quantum just discussed finds itself associated with a charge Ze confined to the charge volume of a normal electron. The simple result is that Z is $(1843)^{\frac{1}{2}}$ or $(1836)^{\frac{1}{2}}$, according to the energy quantum selected. When evaluated Z needs to be either 42·93 of 42·85, both of which are values close to the integer 43. Since Z must be integral if the charge is built up by successive point charge accumulation, we will take a Z value of 43 as the firm basis on which to develop a quark theory. It requires only a marginal spurious energy in space pervaded by high energy matter to create this very short-lived quark state.

The total energy involved in creating the electron-sized quark of $Ze = 43e$ is 945 Mev, corresponding to the 1849 electron mass energy units required. The quark will decay rapidly in search of a stable form. First, bearing in mind that the energy was sourced in electron-positron clusters, we will imagine decay by expansion to a size corresponding to the volume of 43 electrons. The quark energy will then fall to $Z^{5/3}$ electron units, because Z is now proportional to x^3 and energy is proportional to Z^2/x, x being charge radius. The energy becomes about 270 Mev.

Next, let us accept that it is most improbable for a quark of charge $43e$ to form without there being an anti-quark of the same energy and charge $-43e$ formed nearby. They are bound to annihilate one another, being such misfits in the scheme of things. However, their existence is marked by the energy quanta left behind. Each such energy quantum will be deemed to create a pair of particles involving a quark of charge $+e$ or $-e$ (denoted N) which has association with one, two or three electrons or positrons. We are guided here by the systems shown in Figs. 29 and 30. There are four possible systems, as shown in Fig. 37. The polarities can be reversed on each of the four systems, making eight different possible particle aggregations. They all have about the same energy, because N is much larger in energy content than the electron or positron. Thus, if the 270 Mev energy quantum creates pairs involving the N quark and the N anti-quark we may expect each particle unit to have a mass energy of about 135 Mev. Also the creation process will assure approximately equal

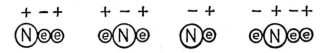

Fig. 37

production of all four of the particle forms shown. The value of N will be set by this energy apportionment. To find N we compute the mass energies of each of the four forms. Taking the electron unit as the base unit we find the following energies:

$$N+0.25 \quad N-0.25 \quad N-0.5 \quad N+0.125$$

For example, the third particle form in Fig. 37 has one N particle, one electron or positron and a negative electric interaction energy of $(3/2)N/(N+1)$ or $-3/2$. Together this gives $N-0.5$.

The average energy of all four forms is $N-0.09375$. It follows that the energy of the N quark is simply $\frac{1}{2}(43)^{5/3}+0.09375$. Now, from an experimental viewpoint, the first two particle forms, being charged, will come together fairly soon and decay. The neutral particle forms will be slightly more stable, but one form, the third shown in Fig. 37, is intrinsically unstable compared with the fourth particle form. Three quark constituents are needed to enhance intrinsic stability, as we saw when we studied the proton. Thus the longest lived particle could well be the fourth shown in Fig. 37. None is likely to survive except for a very limited time, because there will not be many other stabilizing N particles around. They stem from a rather exotic creation process. We conclude that the particle most likely to be detected will be a neutral particle of mass $N+0.125$ electron units. This is $\frac{1}{2}(43)^{5/3}+0.21875$ or 264.105. This is 134.959 Mev. The neutral pion, an important short-lived particle in elementary particle decay, has a measured mass energy of 134.9645 ± 0.0074.

On such encouraging evidence, we will now take the quark of Ze equal to $43e$ seriously and examine its other consequences. In particular, we will search for evidence of stable quarks involving the energy quanta related to paired combinations of two oppositely charged quarks near Ze of $43e$. We look at the quarks in their intermediate decay stage when they occupy the volume corresponding to Z electrons. Thus the formula (166) for Ze interacting with $(Z-1)e$ becomes:

$$E = Z^{5/3} + (Z-1)^{5/3} - \frac{3Z(Z-1)/2}{Z^{1/3} + (Z-1)^{1/3}} \tag{208}$$

E is here expressed in electron mass units or units of 0.511 Mev.

(208) can be simplified as follows:

$$E = Z^{5/3}(5/4 - 25/24Z) \tag{209}$$

for large Z. Had the formula related to interaction between charges of equal Z, its simplified version would become:

$$E = Z^{5/3}(5/4) \tag{210}$$

Had the formula related to interaction between charges of Ze and $(Z-2)e$, its simplified version would have become:

$$E = Z^{5/3}(5/4 - 25/12Z) \tag{211}$$

Below we tabulate the energies of various charge combinations. The middle column shows the charge symbol of the aggregation, which may denote a neutral particle or one of unit or double unit electron charge of either polarity. The energies in the last column are in Mev and are deduced from the formulae (209) and (211).

43:42	±	330·6
43:43	o	337·1
44:42	± ±	336·9
44:43	±	343·6

When these particles collapse by mutual annihilation of charge we may expect to lose the neutral particle. Of the single charged particles only the first in the list can be expected to survive because it has lower energy. Thus we may expect to find two quarks of $(330.6)^{\pm}$ and $(336.9)^{\pm\pm}$ form, respectively.

The numbers give only approximate indications of likely energy but should hold to within about 0.1%.

Is there any evidence that such quarks may exist? The answer is very affirmative, as we see from the empirical studies of MacGregor.* MacGregor was able to show that the masses of all of the fundamental narrow-width hadron resonances could be calculated to an average accuracy of 0·1% using four mass values for quarks. His analysis also included exhaustive treatment of spins, charge splittings, magnetic moments and strangeness quantum numbers. His four quark masses were:

$$M^o = 70\cdot0 \text{ Mev}$$
$$M^{\pm} = 74\cdot6 \text{ Mev}$$
$$S^{\pm} = 330\cdot6 \text{ Mev}$$
$$S^{\pm\pm} = 336\cdot9 \text{ Mev}$$

This encourages belief in the quark process described above, because the two heavier quarks have emerged directly from the theory. As to the two other quarks of MacGregor's analysis, it seems probable, MacGregor implies, that the mass difference between M^o and $M^{\pm}$ stems from the mass difference 4·6 Mev between the charged pion and the neutral pion. For example, the M^o quark could combine with a charged pion to produce a neutral pion plus the quark at 74·6 Mev. Alternatively, the 74·6 Mev quark could combine with the neutral pion and produce the charged pion, leaving the 70·0 Mev neutral quark.

How may the 74·6 quark be produced? Possibly it comes from a paired association with 330·6 Mev in the minimization of formula (166). (167) shows that Q is 74·3 Mev when P is 330·6 Mev. Alternatively, how may the 70·0 Mev quark be produced? It is neutral and could come from the collision of a charged pion and an electron or positron. If the pion energy is denoted P and the electron energy is unity, then $P + 1$ can develop a charged pair of energy $(P + 1)$ comprising energy quanta $(P + 1)$ and $\frac{1}{2}(P + 1)$, as we explained in discussing 'half-synthesis' earlier in this chapter. Upon separation and recombination involving the separation energy $\frac{1}{2}(P + 1)$, this latter energy could form a neutral quark. It corresponds to a mass of $\frac{1}{2}(273\cdot126 + 1)$ electron mass units, or 137·063, which is 70·0 Mev.

* M. H. MacGregor, *Physical Review*, **D10**, 850 (1974).

8

The Cosmic World

The Solar System

In the previous chapter we spoke of creation by reference to the smallest particles from which matter is assembled. Now we turn to the cosmic scene and examine the question of creation of the sun and its planets.

It is conventional to begin with a hypothesis. There was a beginning when the sun was formed by accretion of cosmic dust. Gravity brought the matter together and it nucleated to form the sun. The great mystery is how it all started and another mystery is how the planets formed once the sun became established. The unified physical account presented in our previous chapters gives us a new starting point for addressing these issues, because it has provided a phenomenological account of the nature of gravitation. Gravitation has become dependent upon the structured nature of the vacuum medium. This allows us to contemplate an analogy elsewhere in physics, one, indeed, from which the primary inspiration for the author's development of this whole theory sprang. The analogy arises in the state of ferromagnetism.

The electric interactions between atoms in a crystal can, under certain circumstances prevalent in just a few materials, generate forces we associate with ferromagnetism. The law of electrodynamic interaction developed in Chapter 1 finds application in the author's interpretation of ferromagnetism.* It is the same law as that used to explain gravitational force in this work. Furthermore, we have seen that the gravitational force depends upon the parallel motion of the graviton system, a condition which depends upon ordered motion associated with the lattice structure of the space medium. Random motion in a disordered lattice would suppress the gravitational action.

---

* H. Aspden, *Physics without Einstein*, Sabberton, Southampton, England, p. 48 (1969).

The analogy applies exactly within the ferromagnet. Ferromagnetism vanishes at the Curie temperature when the thermal condition of the crystal lattice is sufficient to upset the interaction forces and upset the critical energy balance favouring ferromagnetism. Logically, therefore, if there was a beginning when cosmic dust began to nucleate to form the sun, then that beginning might have been an event when the space lattice changed from a state of disorder to one of order. Gravitation then appeared, to form the astronomical objects we see today. Conversely, one day we might expect something to trigger the onset of disorder and gravitation may vanish, causing the sun to disintegrate and disperse its matter. Eventually order would be restored and we would begin a new cycle of creation.

This may seem to be mere speculation, but it is speculation with better foundation that the usual nebular hypothesis of creation. The reason is that, because gravitation suddenly appears, a special phenomenon will occur, which could not be foreseen in a system in which gravitation has always existed but matter is created gradually and then nucleated.

Dispersed matter spread over a vast region of space could be expected to contain at least some heavy positive ions and a corresponding number of negative electrons of relatively small mass. The mutual gravitational action of a gas containing such asymmetry in the distribution of charge and mass would cause an initial sun to form with a positive charge Q given by $G^{\frac{1}{2}}M$, M being its mass and G the constant of gravitation. The reason for this is that the mutual gravitational force between two heavy ions causes them to accelerate towards one another at a much higher rate than that operative between two electrons. It only needs a very small degree of ionization to ensure this build-up of central positive charge. The formula is derived in Appendix I.

Eventually, of course, the electrons will arrive to cancel the positive charge and assure the electrical neutrality of the body formed. In the meantime, these electrical effects are all that is necessary to set the character and principally the rotation of the newly formed sun. Also the eventual electrical neutralization by the inflow of electrons induces the creation of the planets.

In explaining these processes, the question of planetary creation will be addressed first. The source of the sun's initial angular momentum (denoted X) will be explained in the next section. Since angular momentum is conserved in the solar system, the value of X is that we measure today as the total angular momentum of the sun's rotation and the planets in orbit. Let R denote the radius of the sun in its primordial form. Given Q, R and X, we can write the following equation:

$$kQ^2/R^2 = X^2/mR^3 \qquad (212)$$

where k is a factor introduced for reasons which will become apparent as we proceed, and m is a mass quantity other than M.

The equation relates the Coulomb interaction between the core charge $+Q$ and the balancing charge $-Q$ on the assumption that the latter charge is held at the surface of the system and associated with matter of mass m which has absorbed all the angular momentum X. k is a factor which qualifies these assumptions. The expression X^2/mR^3 is merely the centrifugal force of the mass m.

R. A. Lyttleton[*] in his book *Mysteries of the Solar System* has explained how magnetic forces exerted within a system of charge by its rotation and self-gravitation will force angular momentum outwards. Thus the transfer of the angular momentum X to a concentrated surface zone is understandable. In a sense this can be thought of as a phenomenon similar to the gyromagnetic reaction already discussed. The reaction angular momentum of the field absorbs angular momentum from the centre of the body and the primary balance of angular momentum is driven to the outer periphery of the rotating system, all as a result of the diamagnetic screening effects within the electrical core.

Once the equation (212) is established, the body is primed to create its satellite system. All that has to happen is for the Q charges to neutralize by slow discharge and as this happens the satellite matter of mass m will leave the main body. It will take up an eventual orbital position governed by gravitational balance between $M - m$ and m and the orbital centrifugal forces of m.

This is all rather simple and it lends itself to immediate verification because we can develop a formula for m/M which can be checked with observation. Note that $GM^2 = Q^2$ and write M as $4\pi\rho_m R^3/3$, where ρ_m is the mass density of the parent body. Replace X by $2MR^2w/5$, the formula for a uniformly dense sphere of mass M and radius R rotating at angular velocity w. Then (212) can become:

$$m/M = 3w^2/25\pi\rho_m Gk \qquad (213)$$

    [*] R. A. Lyttleton, *Mysteries of the Solar System*, Clarendon Press, Oxford, p. 34, 1968.

Now apply this to the sun, noting that the initial angular velocity w of the sun is found by summing the present angular momentum of the solar system and computing w from the above expression for X. This is shown in Appendix II to make w a little greater than 8×10^{-5} rad/s. G is $6 \cdot 67 \times 10^{-8}$ cgs units and ρ_m of the sun, assuming its present value still applies, is $1 \cdot 4$ gm/cc. We then find that if $k = 2$ the planet/sun mass ratio given by (213) is 1/764. The observed value of this mass ratio is 1/745.

Next, let us check this same formula with the Earth's own satellite, the moon. The Earth has a ρ_m value of $5 \cdot 5$ gm/cc and w of the initial Earth before the moon was ejected was, according to Lyttleton,[*] $5 \cdot 5$ hours per revolution or $3 \cdot 2 \times 10^{-4}$ rad/s. This is easily verified by adding the moon's angular momentum in orbit around the Earth to that possessed by the Earth today. In this case we find that if $k = 1$ we obtain from (213) a value of m/M of 1/83. The observed moon/Earth mass ratio is 1/81.

It follows that we have a viable theory of creation of our planetary system if only we can explain why $k = 2$ for the sun and $k = 1$ for the Earth. This is a vital clue to the understanding of the cosmic medium and the source of the sun's initial angular momentum. We find that we need to explore the field energy properties of the space medium of our earlier chapters, but on a cosmic scale.

Cosmic Space

Gravitation has been shown to be an electrodynamic action involving the graviton system of the space medium. The interaction energy associated with this action had two aspects. Firstly, there was a mere deployment of electric field energy between the interacting charge system and the space displacement system. This involved the Neumann potential. Secondly, and governed by this deployment according to the Neumann potential, there was a related amount of energy supplied to the kinetic reaction. This is a kind of thermal energy, generally known as magnetic field energy.

As might be expected, therefore, when matter comes together under gravitational attraction the loss of gravitational potential results in kinetic energy which we assume generates heat and is dispersed. Our observations relate only to the cause, the mysterious force of gravitation, and the ultimate effect, the creation of heat. What happens in

[*] R. A. Lyttleton, *Science Journal*, **5**, 53 (1969).

the intervening stages is not normally considered. It seems probable that if gravitation is a process arising from the involvement of the structured vacuum medium, then the kinetic energy could, in an intermediate stage, be energy associated with motion of that medium. We can then contemplate two kinds of motion, the thermal agitation of the lattice particles and the ordered rotary motion of a whole vast region of the lattice. The disturbances caused by matter are unlikely to affect the universal energy content of the ordered harmonious motion of the space medium depicted in Fig. 22, at least as far as matter acting on matter is concerned. In our next chapter we will see some interesting consequences of gravitational interaction between matter and the lattice of the space medium.

Here, then, is another clue. The energy available from the gravitational accretion of matter forming the sun did not go directly into heat. It passed through a phase in which it sustained the kinetic energy of a body of space itself, as if the space medium associated with this accreting matter were able to move to absorb this energy. The photon unit of our earlier discussions demonstrated the scope for bodily rotation of space within an enveloping non-rotating space. The question posed then is the source of the angular momentum. Now this we have in abundance because the whole C-frame and G-frame system of space, as depicted in Fig. 22 possesses angular momentum on a vast scale. The problem is how to tap this source. It is here that we find the electrical action of the temporary charge Q of the initial sun performs a key role.

In Chapter 2 we saw that a charge would cause displacement of the space lattice, effectively transferring Coulomb energy to the corresponding Coulomb form of charge displacement in the space medium. The charge Q must cause such a displacement in the whole region filled by the accreting solar substance. This system has a special property. It is spherically symmetrical and the displacement is, or rather tends to be, radial from the centre of the system. As electric potential it always tends to minimize and degenerate into kinetic energy. This is not usually possible in an ordered system because it would mean contravening Newton's Third Law of Motion and introducing unidirectional linear momentum. It becomes possible in such a system in the presence of a radial field extending over a large range, because we can have rotation by borrowing angular momentum from the fund of angular momentum of the space medium. Thus the Coulomb energy of the charge Q can find its way into the kinetic energy of rotation of the space medium, transiently, pending the neutralization by $-Q$, and so fix a rotation which is shared by the sun itself. Eventually, much of this kinetic energy is returned as the neutralization process occurs. Some finds its way into normal thermal energy of matter and is dispersed. Perhaps the major part goes into the galactic motion of the sun. However, a small amount is probably retained and sustains the rotation of the space medium within the present sun.

This account lends itself to analysis and, once again, we can take comfort from the very pertinent numerical results which emerge.

Write ρ_0 as the mass density of the lattice system of space which is set in bodily rotation on a large scale. We assume spherical symmetry to permit such rotation without collision with surrounding lattice. Then, taking R now as the radius of such a sphere, the kinetic energy of this rotating space is given by:

$$(1/5)(4\pi R^3/3)\rho_0 w^2 R^2 \tag{214}$$

w is now the angular velocity of this space region.

It is coextensive with a region in which the charge Q is dispersed uniformly and cancelled by displacement generating a uniform space charge of opposite polarity and density σ'. Thus, the electric energy can be calculated as:

$$(3/5)(4\pi R^3/3)^2(\sigma')^2/R \tag{215}$$

We would like these to be equal to signify the possibility that the electric energy may have transferred to kinetic form, assuming that we can find a way of justifying such an action. This would give:

$$\rho_0 w^2 = 4\pi(\sigma')^2 \tag{216}$$

Now we search for such an action. We imagine that the space rotation is about an axis parallel with the universal direction of the spin vector Ω of the space medium. Consider a lattice particle of charge q describing its orbit of radius r at this angular velocity Ω, with its centre carried at speed wR about the remote central axis of the rotating space region. This is illustrated in Fig. 38.

The lattice particle is held in synchronism with all the surrounding particles in the non-rotating space environment as well as with those elsewhere in the rotating region. This puts a constraint on the particles due to their motion about the remote axis. They are displaced in a radial sense in a plane at right angles to this axis, the displacement being inwards or outwards according to the direction of rotation of the space region.

Inspection of Fig. 38 will show that when the two motions are compounded the radius of the particle orbit must vary between

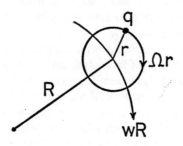

Fig. 38

$r(1 + wR/\Omega r)$ and $r(1 - wR/\Omega r)$ for the condition of synchronous motion to apply. In effect, the particle is moving at a steady speed in orbit about a new centre radially displaced from the remote axis through a distance wR/Ω. This corresponds to an induction of charge of density σ' given by incrementing the radius of a disc of charge density σ by this amount wR/Ω:

$$\pi(\sigma')R^2 = \pi\sigma[(R + wR/\Omega)^2 - R^2] \tag{217}$$

From this:

$$\sigma' = 2\delta w/\Omega \tag{218}$$

The value of σ is, of course, the charge density of the continuum, apart from a change of sign. We know from (132) and the preamble just before (132) at the beginning of Chapter 6 that:

$$m\Omega^2 = 8\pi\sigma q \tag{219}$$

where m is the mass of a lattice particle. As a mass density this becomes $m(\sigma/q)$, which is $8\pi(\sigma/\Omega)^2$ from (219). It is then of interest to see that if we double this, taking account of the equal mass density of the G-frame system, and equate the result to ρ_0, we obtain from (218):

$$\rho_0 w^2 = 4\pi(\sigma')^2 \tag{220}$$

This is the equation (216).

What this means is that the electric energy given by (215) can be converted into the kinetic energy given by (214) by the development of rotation which induces charge displacement owing to the synchronizing constraints, this latter charge displacement replacing the normal direct field displacement but deriving its energy from the pooled energy of the Ω spin of the space medium generally.

The formula (220) gives us immediately a value for w determined by the other parameters of the creation process. We know that σ' is $G^{\frac{1}{2}}\rho_m$. Thus:

$$w = \rho_m(4\pi G/\rho_0)^{\frac{1}{2}} \tag{221}$$

This is independent of R.

Thus a whole expanse of the space medium begins to rotate at this angular velocity w, determined by the mass density ρ_m of the accreting matter. Electrical effects are balanced. The system goes faster and faster as it shrinks in size to the compacted form of a solid body or a gaseous body in equilibrium under its own pressure. The value of w at that time determines how fast the body rotates when created. The value of ρ_0 needs some adjustment for this involvement of ρ_m, but we neglect this in applying formula (221), because our theory tells us that ρ_0 is appreciably higher than the normal mass density associated with matter. Indeed, we will now calculate ρ_0 using the data for w and ρ_m presented above in calculating the masses of the satellite systems of the sun and Earth.

(221) as applied to the sun gives ρ_0 as 257 gm/cc and as applied to the Earth gives ρ_0 as 248 gm/cc. These results are gratifyingly of the same order. However, better than this, there is general agreement with the absolute derivation of ρ_0 from the main theory. We know that ρ_0 is given by:

$$\rho_0 = 2m/d^3 \tag{222}$$

As we saw in Chapter 6 from (155) the mass m is 0·0408 times the mass of the electron, or $3\cdot72 \ 10^{-29}$ gm. The value of r/d was about 0·3029 with r as $1/4\pi$ of the Compton wave-length. Thus d is $6\cdot37 \ 10^{-11}$ cm. From (222) ρ_0 is 288 gm/cc.

It is evident from this that, given the basic theoretical constants of the space medium determined in this work, we can, from (221) and (213), account for the angular momentum and satellite/mother-body mass ratio of planetary systems. The only parameter needed is the mass density of the matter which accretes to form the mother body. There is but one proviso. This arises from the perplexing problem of the factor k in (213). Why should k be 2 for the formation of the sun's satellites and 1 for the formation of the Earth's satellite?

Is this a measure of the uncertainty in the analysis, a 50% factor, or is there some special design in Nature's fabric?

The answer appears once we consider the domain concept of space.

Space Domains

We have used an analogy with ferromagnetism in the introduction to this chapter. This analogy will now be extended to the concept that space has two forms. Our basic space medium was found to have lattice particles immersed in a continuum of charge of opposite polarity. It had a C-frame and a G-frame rotating in the same sense. Thus it involved asymmetry of two kinds, an electrical asymmetry and an angular momentum asymmetry. The need for universal balance suggests that there may be other domains in space within which the lattice particles have the opposite polarities and the continuum also has its charge reversed. Also the direction of the angular momentum vector linked to the parameter Ω could change from one domain to the next. In the universe overall there could be balance, that is no net angular momentum and as many anti-lattice particles as lattice particles. A vacuum of space and anti-space domains is suggested.

Potentially each star, or pair of stars if binary, is a candidate for its own space domain. There is unlikely to be any gravitational action between matter in separate space domains. Hence gravitational interaction between stars would seem to be precluded on this model. This is not so, because, although stars formed in different domains may be de-coupled gravitationally at the time they were formed, they migrate across domain boundaries and they are gravitationally coupled when sharing the same domain. A loosely-connected gravitational action can then be envisaged as an average effect acting only between nearby stars. It is as if they are coupled by a chain subjected to sporadic jerks so that some links are disconnected at any given moment. Such a chain can, nevertheless, convey forces, especially if each link has the inertia of a star.

The need for such domains is soon apparent when we trace the source of the angular momentum needed to create a star. Now, as was explained by reference to equations (97) and (98) in the chapter on quantum mechanics, an energy E fed to the space medium involves an angular momentum addition of E/Ω and half the energy goes into kinetic energy locally. Conversely, if the space medium yields an energy E as gravitational energy it loses angular momentum E/Ω and kinetic energy $\frac{1}{2}E$. This angular momentum is assumed to go to the star.

On this basis we can write the gravitational potential of a lattice particle of mass m as:

$$\Phi m = \Omega H_m \qquad (223)$$

where H_m is the angular momentum released by each unit cell of the space lattice. This is an angular momentum of $\Phi m/\Omega$ per mass m or $\frac{1}{2}\Phi\rho_0/\Omega$ per cc. Φ is the gravitational potential of a star of mass M distant R from the region under study. Thus the total angular momentum of the star becomes:

$$(AM) = \int_0^D \tfrac{1}{2}(GM/R)\rho_0(4\pi R^2)(1/\Omega)dR \qquad (224)$$

This supposes that the domain is spherical and of radius D. The result is:

$$(AM) = \pi GMD^2\rho_0/\Omega \qquad (225)$$

D is given by:

$$D^2 = S\Omega/\pi G\rho_0 \qquad (226)$$

where S is the parameter angular momentum/mass of the star.

Now from (221) we can show that for any star this parameter S is simply related to mass/radius. This does not vary much between stars. The sun is typical and reliable as an estimate of the order of magnitude of this quantity S. For the sun the angular momentum is about $3 \cdot 2 \; 10^{50}$ cgs units (at creation) and M is $2 \; 10^{33}$. Thus, from (226) with G as $6 \cdot 67 \; 10^{-8}$ cgs and Ω as $7 \cdot 8 \; 10^{20}$ s^{-1}, as known from the quantum mechanical chapter, we find a value of D dependent upon ρ_0. This mass density ρ_0 has just been shown to be 288 gm/cc. Accordingly, D becomes $4 \cdot 6 \; 10^{20}$ cm or 480 light years.

We may expect the space domains to be measured in hundreds of light years from this account. Note that the domain boundary limits on the integration are necessary in (226). Otherwise the angular momentum fed to the star would be infinite. It increases as D^2. If, on the other hand, we say that the domain extends far enough to include numerous stars in proportion to D^3 then the angular momentum increases in proportion to D^5 and the angular momentum per star is still proportional to D^2. There must then be domains bounded in the manner indicated.

Today we find stars clustered together in regions, as if the gravitational effects between adjacent stars have brought them in closer proximity than at creation. There are several stars close enough to the sun to lie within the single domain just discussed. Such speculation, however, runs contrary to the popular idea of the expansion of the universe, and we will not develop this theme. Instead, we will adhere to the domain theory now developed and consider events as the star crosses a domain boundary.

We know that during the transit there is a breakdown of gravitational action across the boundary. This we will discuss later from the viewpoint of events on Earth as our Earth is affected by the corresponding phenomenon. The main point is the balance of the charge Q. Until the primordial sun forms its satellites it rotates with its full initial angular velocity. Thus Q is preserved in the core in balance with the radial displacement effect discussed by reference to Fig. 38. The charge $-Q$ has settled at the periphery of the sun and is kept there by the balance of charge in the space medium. Note that the radial displacement of lattice charge in space creates the uniform charge distribution within the rotating space medium but it also leaves a shell of charge at the surface. The state of electrical balance is that shown in Fig. 39.

A key issue is whether the material substance of the body has a larger radius or a smaller radius than the rotating space region. We have assumed them to be coextensive but they may not be quite coextensive. Much will depend upon whether the body developed its form in good time before the arrival of negative charge. If it developed in stages then the space region could well be of smaller radius and the body thereby inclined to shed a higher proportion of its mass as a satellite.

Therefore, in Fig. 39, both alternatives are shown. The full circle depicts the form of the body and the broken circle depicts the form of the space region. There is charge balance in both of the upper figures.

Now let us see what happens when the whole system finds itself on the other side of a space domain boundary. This is shown for both systems in the lower part of Fig. 39. The space charges have reversed because the rotation of the space medium has retained its inertial effects. We presume that the direction of the spin vector Ω

is much the same between adjacent domains. There is now a complete unbalance of charge. Magnetic effects due to rotation will appear and transfer angular momentum to outer regions and the matter charge $-Q$ will be set in centrifugal balance with the Coulomb interaction. In one case, however, where the matter charge $-Q$ is within the space boundary, the Coulomb interaction is

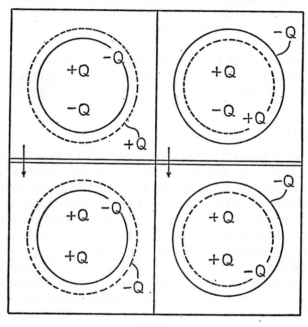

Fig. 39

$2Q^2/R^2$, whereas in the other case, where the matter charge $-Q$ is located outside the space boundary, the Coulomb interaction is Q^2/R^2. It all depends upon whether the $-Q$ charge at the space boundary is effective in producing any force on the matter charge. Thus the factor k in (213) will be 2 for the sun and 1 for the Earth, under these circumstances. No doubt the matter shed by the Earth in forming the moon resulted in the Earth's space boundary settling outside the eventual form of the Earth.

The key assumption made above is that the centrifugal balance between charge and surface matter is established before the system decays by electric discharge. This is very probable when one considers energy deployment. The basic energy is still in the kinetic form of the rotating space medium. The polarity reversal of the space medium in crossing the boundary is not an actual reversal. It is an apparent reversal. The body has moved from one region to another. The synchronizing constraints in each region will assure that energy is available if needed to sustain a transient condition. Thus the $2Q$ charge can exist and will disappear as the space region slows down and enough electrons can move in to assure a balance. Bear in mind that the initial crossing of the boundary would destroy the gravitational field momentarily causing the negative charge in the surface regions to be displaced from the surface of the body. It takes a little time to react to the attraction of the central charge and the centrifugal motion seemingly is established in this interval.

Geomagnetism

Our next question is that of the effects on the Earth of crossing a space domain boundary. We must, even after the many eons since our Earth was created, be crossing these space domain boundaries as the whole solar system progresses on its course through space. It travels at about 390 km/s, as we saw from the opening words in Chapter 3. At this speed it takes 770 years to travel one light year. It would take about 700,000 years to traverse the space domain calculated in the above example. Therefore, every 700,000 or so years we should suddenly experience a violent upset as gravitation relaxes in effect for the few seconds of transit. Also we should find that the polarity reversal of σ' causes a magnetic reversal of the Earth's field.

In this connection we can calculate the magnetic moment produced by the residual charge Q of the Earth today. This charge is positive at the present time. Its polarity is set opposite to that of σ' as induced by the rotation of the space frame with the Earth. Magnetic effects are evidenced by disturbances of the lattice particle system. The charge σ' cannot itself induce a magnetic field because it arises from a displacement of the lattice. Thus it is only the compensating charge Q associated with matter rotating with the frame that can generate a magnetic effect. There is of course a balance charge $-Q$ at the boundary which is part of the system of matter present and this also has to be taken into account. Indeed, it may be shown that the latter charge develops twice the magnetic moment of the distributed core charge. The difference is the same in magnitude as that due to the distributed charge but has the direction we associate with negative charge. It is this double action which causes the field to be similar to that of a dipole at the centre of the Earth.

The earth's magnetic moment is simply $1/2c$ times the electric charge velocity moment, or:

$$(1/2c)(2/5)(4\pi\sigma'/3)R^5w \qquad (227)$$

From (218) and the fact that σ is e/d^3:

$$\sigma' = 2ew/\Omega d^3 \qquad (228)$$

Then, since Ω is $c/2r$, we put (228) in (227) to find a magnetic moment of:

$$16\pi er R^5 w^2/15d^3c^2 \qquad (229)$$

In this expression er is the Bohr Magneton, known from experiment to be $9 \cdot 27 \ 10^{-21}$ cgs units. d was shown above to be $6 \cdot 37 \ 10^{-11}$ cm. For the Earth today w is $7 \cdot 26 \ 10^{-5}$ rad/s. c is $3 \ 10^{10}$ cm/s.

The resulting value of the geomagnetic moment is very critically dependent upon R, the radius of the space medium rotating with the Earth. Thus, if R is $6 \cdot 45 \ 10^8$ cm the magnetic moment is $7 \cdot 86 \ 10^{25}$ cgs units. If R is $6 \cdot 50 \ 10^8$ cm the magnetic moment is $8 \cdot 17 \ 10^{25}$ cgs units. In fact, the radius of the Earth is $6 \cdot 38 \ 10^8$ cm and the geomagnetic moment measured is $8 \cdot 06 \ 10^{25}$ cgs units.

These are very significant results, which bear out the essential validity of the theory presented. Evidently the Earth's space boundary is about 100 km above the Earth's surface on this theory. There is the question of the direction of the geomagnetic moment and the precession of the poles needs explanation, but we do have here the essential foundations for an understanding of the nature of the geomagnetic field.

It is feasible to think of the Earth's magnetic field reversing at times when the Earth is carried across a space domain boundary. By studying the evidence of the Earth's magnetic field reversals some indication of the existence, the size, and the form of the space domains should become available. We have inferred their approximate size from the theory of the space medium and the hypothesis that the known mass of the sun is typical of stellar mass generally. It remains a mystery as to why space domains of this particular size should form. To probe that question is to seek to understand why the stars have a particular mass and such questions must be deferred at this time. However, we can picture the reversal pattern of the geomagnetic field for a simple domain structure. As each domain has about the same size a simple cubic domain structure seems an appropriate choice. The results will be an approximation only, inasmuch as all stars do not have the same mass/radius parameter. To estimate the degree of approximation let us consider the extreme example of a red giant star in comparison with the sun. Betelgeux is said by Jeans* to be about 40 times as massive as the sun and to occupy 25,000,000 times as much volume. The mass/radius parameter is 0·137 compared with the sun. The value of D given by (226) is 0·37 for this red giant star, compared with the sun's domain radius D at creation. However, a red giant is believed to be the decaying form of a star, rather than the form it may have upon initial creation. Since the majority of stars are similar to the sun we can, therefore, expect a reasonably-representative pattern of magnetic field reversals to emerge from a choice of a simple cubic structured domain system. A reversal period of the order of 700,000 years is to be expected for motion parallel with a main axis of the cubic domain structure. In general, however, a motion will be inclined to such an axis and the planes separating domain boundaries will be crossed more frequently than this.

In Fig. 40 the hypothetical pattern of reversals due to motion through cubic domain space is shown in a time scale measured in millions of years before the present time. The solar system is imagined to move in a straight line through domain space over this period of time, though it does move in a slight arc owing to the galactic motion. The inclination of the line with the domain cube axes is chosen deliberately to give results which resemble the observed reversal sequence and the time scale has been matched accordingly. The names assigned to the reversals are those used conventionally to designate these events. There is a reasonably close correlation. The interesting result, however, is that such an erratic pattern of events lends itself to decoding in this way. The author believes that this is affirmative support for the domain theory suggested, especially as the size of the domains derived from the empirical data fit is in close accord with that calculated for the sun. Note that the analysis leading to (226) required D to be the radius of a spherical domain. The corresponding cube dimension would be smaller than this. The data in Fig. 40 suggest a domain cube size of about 400,000 years at the

* J. H. Jeans, *The Stars in their Courses*, Cambridge University Press, p. 92 (1931).

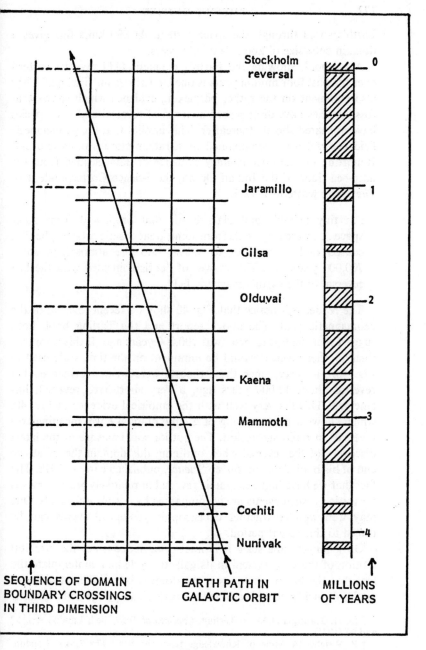

Fig. 40

Earth's speed through the space system. At 390 km/s this gives a domain cube size of about 500 light years.

A textbook showing the Earth's magnetic field reversal pattern over the past four million years is one by Tarling and Tarling.* They also comment on the rather perplexing evidence which shows that fossil species have disappeared at times of reversal and new species have appeared shortly thereafter. This implies that the geomagnetic field reversal was accompanied by a rather more traumatic event. Reporting on the documentary evidence of data gleaned from the deep-sea floor of the Indian Ocean, the Science Correspondent of *The Times* wrote in 1972:†

> . . . tiny metallic and glass beads that originated from outer space . . . were fragments from some great cosmic catastrophe that caused molten particles to splash into the atmosphere some 700,000 years ago. The shower of debris coincided with the last reversal of the earth's magnetic field.

The reader will notice that Fig. 40 shows a recent reversal of the geomagnetic field. The above report and the Tarling book both suggest that the last reversal was 700,000 years ago. If this were true then another reversal would be imminent on the time scale used in Fig. 40. However, since these reports were written evidence of a reversal about 12,000 years ago, a very short-lived reversal, has emerged. This fits very well with the empirical evidence in Fig. 40, which shows a near crossing of a cube domain edge, meaning two reversals in rapid succession. The author was unaware of the latest discovery of the reversal when outlining this domain theory at the end of his book *Modern Aether Science*, published early in 1972. The fact that we have had a magnetic reversal in relatively recent times is reassuring if such events are accompanied by cosmic upheavals. One may well wonder whether catastrophic geological events can be traced to this recent period.

On a longer time scale it is interesting to consider the circuital motion of the solar system in its galactic cycle and contemplate the fact that the Earth would cross the domain boundaries at different angles of incidence with a four-fold periodicity per galactic cycle. If

* D. H. Tarling and M. P. Tarling, *Continental Drift*, Bell, London, pp. 52 and 66 (1971).

† P. Wright, 'A Mine of Knowledge from the Sea', *The Times*, London, August 17 (1972).

the gravitational field between matter in the Earth is disturbed when the domain boundaries are traversed, the faster the crossing, the less the disturbance. The crossing will be most rapid when the Earth approaches the boundary in the normal direction. If it approaches a boundary at a low angle it will take much longer to traverse it. Indeed, it seems statistically possible for an approach to be at such a low angle that the Earth could disintegrate on reaching the domain boundary. The probability is very small but it is a consequence of this theory and one might wonder whether the asteroids really originated in a planet broken up in this way.

These ideas are highly speculative but take encouragement from the researches of Steiner.* He has made an extensive study of the possible correlation between geological events and the galactic motion and concluded that the constant of gravitation G may, in some way, depend upon the period in the galactic cycle. The theoretical interpretation of such data is difficult in view of the uncertainties in the present state of cosmological theory, particularly so far as concerns the variation of G. The problem is further confused by the expanding Earth hypothesis which is dependent upon a slowly varying G. Yet Einstein's theory hardly permits G to vary and the author's theory presented in this work requires G to be as constant as the charge-mass ratio of the electron. One feels that if the latter were to change then all other parameters, such as the speed of light and the dimensions of the space lattice and even energy, would change as well. The author therefore favours the supposition that G is constant but only acts between matter within specific domains of space. This renders G effectively dependent upon the position of our planet as far as geological events are concerned and seems to offer scope for relating geological events and galactic motion. However, far more research is needed before these ideas can leave the realm of speculation. Meanwhile, reverting to the statement above that there would be a four-fold periodicity of gravitational upset in the galactic cycle if the space domain ideas hold, the author draws attention to another paper by Steiner† in which he writes:

If Phanerozoic geological history incorporates any periodicities, they are of the order of 60 or perhaps 70 million years. . . . The galactic periodicity of the solar system is, however, approximately

* J. Steiner, *Jour. Geol. Soc. Australia*, **14**, 99 (1967).
† J. Steiner, 'Geology', p. 89 (1973).

274 million years, representing the length of the cosmic year, or one revolution around the galactic centre.

The author's ideas on space domains and their correlation with geomagnetic field reversals and geological disturbances are also presented in a paper in *Catastrophist Geology*, **2**, 42 (1977).

9

General Discussion

The 2.7° Cosmic Background

In the opening paragraph of Chapter 3 reference was made to the recently reported detection of aether drift by an article in the May, 1978, issue of *Scientific American*.* The closing words of this article were:

> It is possible, indeed likely, that there are large-scale structures that play an essential role in determining the nature of the universe. With recent measurements of the large-scale clustering of galaxies and the anisotropy of the cosmic background radiation we may be just beginning to detect that structure.

This is the outlook at the present time. It bears out the author's case for examining the space medium to find domain structures which relate to the creation of stars. The aether, as a real medium, must be revived in a new form. Unfortunately, there is far too much emphasis today on a direction of research which is based upon undue extrapolation of relativistic theory. The idea that G holds and that gravitation exists within matter of immense densities transcending the electric interactions in such matter and leading to the so-called black hole is very far-reaching speculation. The idea that time reverses is also far-reaching speculation. It captures imagination. An example of its consequences is available concerning the cosmic background radiation question and the measured 2·7° K temperature.

Davies,† writing in *Nature Physical Science*, exploits the coincidence that the energy density of starlight in our galaxy is comparable with this black body background. He deduces a temperature of 2·4° K from his hypothesis that:

* R. A. Muller, *Scientific American*, **238**, 64 (1978).
† P. C. W. Davies, *Nature Physical Science*, **240**, 3 (1972).

an observer at the present epoch should be able to detect black body background caused by the starlight of the subsequent cycle.

His ideas involve domains in space with oppositely-directed time sense, separated by regions in which time has no direction. Thus the cosmic background temperature measured in space anisotropy experiments is caused by radiation from the future. One may then wonder where we will be led by our researches if such interpretations find favour. However, Davies has provided a theory for the temperature of radiation, albeit rather lower at $2 \cdot 4°$ K than the recognized value of $2 \cdot 7°$ K, and any challenge should offer a similar result.

Let us see whether the theory put forward in the previous chapters sheds any light on this problem. We are concerned with the temperature of space itself, a temperature associated with what is called cosmic background radiation. Temperature is a property we associate with the thermal motion state of matter. It governs the transfer of energy from A to B. There is no energy transfer when the temperature at A is the same as that at B. Therefore, temperature is a measure of the intrinsic capacity of something at A to release energy when the so-called temperature is above the norm. If the condition at A is such that it can withold energy because this energy is trapped by local field conditions then this energy will not participate in the transfer process. The question then is whether it could manifest itself as a temperature as judged by the electromagnetic radiation field and yet remain secure against dissipation.

Consider the temperature expression:

$$T = T_0 + H^2/8\pi kN - \Phi m/k \qquad (230)$$

Here k is Boltzmann's constant. N is the number of particles per cc. sharing the kinetic reaction energy of a magnetic field of intensity H, Φ is the local gravitational potential and m is the mass of the lattice particle of our space medium.

The theory presented has indicated that the magnetic field energy must be stored in a kinetic reaction state, even in the vacuum medium. It remains available for recovery as soon as the current producing the field subsides. Similarly, because gravitation is an electrodynamic phenomenon on the theory presented, we can regard the gravitational potential of each lattice particle as having released energy which must be stored locally by the thermal agitation of the particle. We suppose, as our hypothesis, that T_0, the basic temperature of the system, is the equilibrium temperature governing energy transfer by thermal action but that T is the temperature measured by our frequency radiation detectors.

The value of k is $1.38 \ 10^{-16}$ erg/°K. We know that N is $1/d^3$, where d is $6.37 \ 10^{-11}$ cm, supposing that in the vacuum medium only the lattice particles can conform to the Boltzmann energy conditions. Thus N is $3.87 \ 10^{30}$. Thus the highest magnetic field we can produce would not raise the temperature by any measurable amount. A value of H of 10^6 cgs units corresponds to a temperature of $0.000075°$ K.

The gravitational effect is more interesting. It does not depend upon N. Note that the energy has not been set equal to $3kT/2$, as is normal. Readers are reminded that early in Chapter 5 it was shown that the lattice particle has only two degrees of freedom and this means that energy is related to kT, as assumed in (230). From (155) it was shown that m is 0.0408 times the mass of the electron. Thus m/k is found to be $2.7 \ 10^{-13}$. In these same cgs units the value of the gravitational potential attributable to the combined effect of the sun and the Earth at a position near the Earth's surface is $9.49 \ 10^{12}$. (230) therefore does give a measurable temperature of:

$$T = T_0 + (9.49 \ 10^{12})(2.7 \ 10^{-13}) \tag{231}$$

in the immediate environment of the Earth. Note that the gravitational potential is really negative, making T greater than T_0. Also note that if we look at the vacuous medium near the Earth we must expect T_0 to be zero. The observed background temperature of space near the Earth given by (231) should then, in theory, be $2.6°$ K. This is quite good agreement with the actual value of $2.7°$ K. It is better than the value obtained by Davies. The test is also a direct verification of the mass of the lattice particle.

The gravitational potential just presented is derived from $G(M_s/R_a + M_e/R_e)$, where G is the constant of gravitation $6.67 \ 10^{-8}$, M_s is the solar mass $1.989 \ 10^{33}$, R_a is the astronomical unit $1.496 \ 10^{13}$, M_e is the Earth mass $5.977 \ 10^{27}$ and R_e is the Earth radius $6.378 \ 10^8$, all in cgs units.

Gravitational Potential

It has just been argued that there is a kind of gravitational action between matter and the lattice particle system of space. We need, therefore, to examine more closely this idea that space can interact gravitationally with matter. First, note that we associate gravitation with a state of disturbance of the space medium caused by the presence of matter. If there were no matter disturbing the space medium, there would be perfect balance in the space medium, assuring that the lattice particles do not interact in the gravitational sense with other lattice particles. The electrodynamic interaction is not in evidence.

Now, when matter is present we expect an interaction with the lattice particles, because matter acting on matter does so via inducing a reaction in space and this is, presumably, provided by, or at least mainly by, the lattice particles. The doubt can arise because we have assumed that the E-frame or C-frame of space comprises exclusively the q charges or so-called lattice particles. Yet, we have spoken of the energy exchanges between electrons (or positrons) and lattice particles in order to set the r/d ratio used in deriving the fine structure constant. There could be a sparse population of electrons amongst the lattice particles forming the E-frame. One effect would be to increase the temperature of space as just determined. Since temperature is proportional to mass and relative population, the mass of the electron, being 24·52 times that of the lattice particle, would result in an increase in the temperature of the cosmic background by 0·1° K for one electron per 600 or so lattice particles. The 0·1° K discrepancy between theory and observation in the previous section could therefore suggest such an electron presence in the E-frame of the space medium.

It is of interest to note that the electron population contemplated is of a slightly higher order of magnitude than that we associate with the free electron population in conductors. Electrons, whether part of matter or part of the E-frame, may therefore exhibit the effects of gravitational potential φ in common with the lattice particles. φ at the Earth's surface is 9·49 10^{12} cgs units, making φ/c^2 1·06 10^{-8} for use in the electron g-factor correction at the end of Chapter 5.

It remains to explain why we can take gravitational potential and assign the full interaction energy to the space particle involved in the interaction. It was important to the derivation of Einstein's law of gravitation in Chapter 2 that this gravitational interaction energy had a distribution in space as given by Fig. 12. How, then, can it be correct to presume that this energy is all vested in one of the interacting components?

The answer to this is that the distribution of energy given by Fig. 12 applies only to interaction between finite and separated bodies or particles of matter in isolation. If the distribution deduced for Fig. 12

were applied to a system comprising a particle of matter or a central body surrounded by space of uniform and infinite extent and having a mass interaction with the matter particle, we would obtain infinite energy densities in the space near the particle. This is precluded by the need for energy to disperse within the constraints of the overall interaction.

For such a system the reaction energy associated with gravitation optimizes differently and this causes us to reconsider the analysis leading to Fig. 12. We know that n is a positive integer over the range of x between 0 and r and that it is as low as possible to satisfy the optimization condition. Putting M as the mass of the central particle at 0 and m as an interacting mass distant r, we may represent the general distribution indicated by Fig. 12, using positive energy distributions, by the formulae:

$$\frac{kGMmx^n}{r^{n+2}} \tag{232}$$

for x between 0 and r, and:

$$\frac{kGMm}{x^2} \tag{233}$$

for x greater than r. Integration with respect to x over all space gives:

$$\frac{kGMm}{r}\left(\frac{1}{n+1}+1\right) \tag{234}$$

With $n=1$ and $k=\frac{2}{3}$, the result corresponding to the Einstein gravitation law and applying between discrete bodies:

$$\frac{GMm}{r} \tag{235}$$

follows from (234) as the gravitational potential energy of the system.

Now, if we regard m as $4\pi r^2\rho dr$, where ρ is the mass density of a uniform medium enveloping M and we consider a spherical shell of radius r centred on M, the energy density at radius x, as given by (232) and (233) combined, becomes:

$$\int_x^\infty \frac{kGMx^{n-2}dr}{3r^n} + \int_0^x \frac{kGMr^2dr}{3x^4} \tag{236}$$

Note that we have divided by $4\pi x^2$.

For $n = 1$ the integral expression in (236) is infinite. For other
the solution is:

$$\frac{kGM\rho}{x}\left(\frac{1}{n-1}+\frac{1}{3}\right) \tag{23}$$

Now, we know that n is as low as possible. $n = 1$ is precluded by th
infinite solution. Therefore $n = 2$. Putting this in (234) gives the usu
gravitational potential energy (235) when k is $\frac{3}{4}$. Thus, we can dete
mine the energy density at a distance x from M in the space mediu
by putting $n = 2$ and $k = \frac{3}{4}$ in (237). The result is $GM\rho/x$, exactly th
gravitational potential energy attributed to the interaction betwee
M and ρ. Hence we have justified the remarkable fact that we ca
take an energy known to be distributed in space and assign this to th
locality of the interacting mass in the space medium. This great
strengthens the explanation for the temperature of the cosm
background radiation proposed in this work.

The Gravitational Deflection of Light

It is an acclaimed achievement of Einstein's theory that the defle
tion of light by the solar gravitational field follows from the law
gravitation derived using that theory. Since the same law has bee
obtained earlier in this work in terms of retardation of the electr
dynamic interaction we need not dwell on the problem of gravit
tional deflection of light. However, the author has some reservatio
about the mathematical technique used by relativists to deduce th
deflection and a few comments seem appropriate.

Firstly, the speed of light is justified theoretically by Maxwell
theory once it is accepted that c is the parameter relating electr
magnetic and electrostatic units of charge. This relationship wa
established earlier in this work by arguments based upon Fig. 1
The parameter c used in that figure was shown to be halved t
retardation. $\frac{1}{2}c$ became the speed of the lattice particle in its natur
cyclic oscillations at the space frequency. Thus, indirectly, the spee
of light at any position in the vacuum medium depends upon th
speed of the bound lattice particles.

The question then is how gravitation may affect this speed. W
have just seen that local gravitational potential is stored in the kineti
'thermal' agitation of the lattice particles. This local thermal energ

deemed to come from a depletion of the local energy of the lattice particle and its counter-balance moving at the space frequency. Thus:

$$\Phi m + m(c/2)^2 = \text{constant} \qquad (238)$$

Here Φ is taken to be positive because Φm is the gravitational energy of a lattice particle of mass m expressed as a kinetic energy.

Note that in explaining the nature of gravitation a mass in motion with the lattice at the space frequency was set in dynamic balance with the mass of energy added to gravitons moving in counter-balance with the lattice. The energy we associate with matter has an equal counterpart hidden in the space metric. Thus energy quantities and mass quantities need to be doubled in many instances to correctly represent conditions within the vacuum medium. When we speak of gravitational potential we restrict ourselves to the matter system moving with the lattice frame. Now, as we saw in deriving (97) in Chapter 5, the orbital displacement of lattice particles involves equal change of electric displacement energy and kinetic energy and, for dynamic balance, there are equal related changes in the graviton system. If we consider the total energy system, the kinetic energy of the lattice plus that of the graviton system can be deployed into 'thermal' motion to represent the basic gravitational potential energy and the equal amount of displacement energy can be regarded as counterpart energy of this gravitational potential hidden in the space metric. In this way (238) is fully justified.

In applying Boltzmann's constant to this lattice system, we regard the lattice particle more as a molecule comprising the mass m of the particle plus the counterpart mass m of the coupled graviton system. However, it is correct to use a mass of m in (230) because this equation represents energy in the matter frame only. Nevertheless, the coupling with the graviton frame assures that only one temperature is manifested by the space medium. The graviton system does not have its own temperature related to graviton mass.

The value of c given by (238) is less than the value of c for a zero gravitational potential. It is less by $2\Phi m/c$, exactly the value needed to explain the observed deflection of light by a gravitational field and in exact conformity with the result given by the Einstein formula.

The Clock Paradox

A report in 1972* on an experiment performed by Hafele and
Keating† began with the words:

> Two American physicists with four atomic clocks flew around the
> world in search of the solution to the famous clock paradox raised
> by Einstein's relativity theory. They discovered that you age a
> fraction of a second while in flight, but the amount depends on the
> direction in which you are going.

It needs a rather special definition of one's rate of ageing in order
to arrive at this conclusion from experiments on atomic clocks, but
the Hafele–Keating experiment is certainly very important. It should
be repeated at different times of year, however, in order to make its
results more conclusive.

The rate of an atomic clock changes with its speed. This is to be
expected from the Ives–Stilwell experiment mentioned in Chapter 3,
which demonstrated the change of frequency of the spectral emission
from fast moving atoms. This experiment on the so-called transverse
Doppler effect was claimed to verify relativistic time dilation, and so
confirm Einstein's Theory of Special Relativity. In Chapter 3 we saw
how it may be explained without our conception of time variation
and by retaining the traditional view that time has a universal
constancy. The same argument applies to the flying clock experiment,
which relies upon the same formulae insofar as it is a test of Einstein's
theory.

The clock paradox is a paradox evoked by applying relativity to
the rate of time sensed by two travellers on separate journeys which
they make at different velocities. When they meet again to compare
their measure of the time taken there should be some confusion. The
assumption is that they travel on outward and homeward journeys at
uniform velocity and are only subject to acceleration momentarily
when they turn around. Special relativity requires each clock to slow
down when viewed by the bearer of the other clock, a rather para-
doxical situation. The Ives–Stilwell experiment was concerned with
time dilation as viewed by the observer at rest in the laboratory, but
the atoms were moving fast enough for the motion of the laboratory,
owing to the Earth's rotation about its axis, to be inconsequential.

* G. Wick, *New Scientist*, **53**, 261 (1972).
† J. Hafele and R. Keating, *Science*, **177**, 166 (1972).

Therefore, whether the experiment indicates an effect caused by speed relative to the moving observer on the Earth, relative to the non-rotating electromagnetic reference frame or, indeed, relative to some absolute space frame is not clear.

Certainly, the flying clock experiments had to take account of the component of speed attributable to the Earth's rotation. In this sense they could be said to relate more to the effects of centrifugal acceleration and so involve Einstein's General Theory of Relativity. The formulae are the same. This means that the experiment has little bearing upon the clock paradox, which remains a basic weakness at the roots of relativity. It is not a weakness and there is no paradox if one regards relativity philosophically as merely providing a technique useful in interpretation of physical phenomena. The weakness arises once one accepts relativity as physics and as sufficient foundation for phenomenological explanation.

The flying clock experiment also demonstrated the time dependence of clocks upon the gravitational potential. The clocks were carried at a high altitude in their journeys around the world. Hence their exposure to such a change of potential. In this regard the earlier experimental results of Pound and Rebka were confirmed.* The spectral frequencies emitted by an atom are higher, the higher the atom above the ground. This is a curious phenomenon. If the photon were a corpuscle having a frequency related to its energy it should, on this experimental basis, lose energy as it falls and gain energy as it rises. This seems the wrong way about. Yet if the photon is a wave one also has the problem of understanding how it can change frequency when moving through a gravitational field. Relativity provides suitable formulae but does not answer these physical questions.

The obvious answer to the author is to say that the atom exchanges energy with the space medium in dependence upon the local gravitational potential. Less photon energy is involved at the higher magnitudes of gravitational potential. Thus, bearing in mind that gravitational potential is negative, we have a higher magnitude of potential closer to the Earth's surface. This means that more related kinetic energy is held trapped in the space medium. This is energy which is proportional to the mass content of the atom. If then the atom produces a photon not all of the mass energy released is in the

* R. V. Pound and G. A. Rebka, *Phys. Rev. Lett.* **3**, 439 (1959) and **4**, 337 (1960).

form which governs the photon frequency. There will be a shift of the frequency spectrum towards the red end in proportion to the magnitude of the local gravitational potential. The red shift will be greater at lower altitudes. Hence the photon frequency will be higher at higher altitudes. This is merely a consequence of $E = Mc^2$ and the Principle of Equivalence. It does not need any support from Einstein's General Theory of Relativity. Indeed, the red shift as explained by General Relativity is not a strong test of that theory, as we have already seen in Chapter 2, where Dicke was quoted on this subject.

Mass-energy Equivalence

At this stage it is appropriate to come back to a theme mentioned in Chapter 3 when we discussed the transverse Doppler effect. Does electric interaction energy between charges in motion exhibit mass? This was the problem raised by Brillouin. We found in Chapter 3 that the time dilation evidence derived from the spectral emissions of atoms moving at high speed could be explained if the interaction energy does not increase as does the mass of the electron when speed increases.

The problem is really one concerning the seat of any mass resulting from such interaction energy. One could say that the mass effect is shared between two interacting charges. For example, the negative interaction energy component due to the Coulomb interaction between an electron and positron could be said to result in an equal decrement of mass of these two particles when they are accelerated as a pair to high speeds. In the case of the interaction between a proton and an electron, however, would the decrement be shared equally or in proportion to the masses of the two particles? In the latter case what happens if the interaction energy changes suddenly owing to a spectral emission? Does the inertia of the proton or its independence from the electron somehow preclude the 'relativistic' speed component of the interaction energy from governing the photon energy exchange? If so we would have the interaction energy exhibiting mass when we sense the behaviour of the hydrogen atom inertially but not exhibiting mass when we sense the spectral behaviour of the atom.

These are problems which need confirmed solutions. Very probably interaction energy due to Coulomb interactions does exhibit mass properties even when the interacting charges are not tightly bound in a rigid aggregation. This is suggested by the results obtained in Chapter 1 when electrodynamic properties were discussed. The inertial properties of a reacting system of electric charges were part of the case used to explain magnetic fields. If the reacting charges are similar in their mass properties the interaction between them would be a shared property as well. From accepted physics one can obtain many formulae purporting to give answers to all these questions. However, they are seldom applied in a way which confirms that they are valid. Uncertainties must therefore remain in physics which seeks to be all-embracing. They become the driving force which makes further research worthwhile. The mass to be assigned to the Coulomb interaction is one such question. It is fundamental to the issue of time dilation. Nevertheless, the author believes that the approach to this problem as just presented may well prove itself as we come to understand more about the nature of mass.

Moving E-frames

The optical experiments in Chapter 3 were reconciled by introducing the idea of a moving electromagnetic reference frame. This is a non-rotating frame of reference which moves linearly with the space lattice and which is formed by the rotation of a whole region of the lattice. The lattice particle structure has angular momentum attributable to such rotation and this has been called into account in discussing the creation of the solar system. Once in rotation such a region defines its own E-frame. Though non-rotating, this E-frame is determined by lattice particles which not only share the lattice region rotation but have the synchronous cyclic motion shared by all such particles within a vast space domain at the space frequency $m_e c^2/h$.

How can such a system of lattice particles move along a linear trajectory, as must happen if the Earth contains such a rotating region? The Earth's electromagnetic reference frame shares its linear motion through space. Would not the particles collide with those in surrounding space in the path ahead of the Earth's motion? Consideration shows that any build-up of particles at the leading surface of a moving space region would be matched by a particle deficit at the rear surface. This would set up electric fields through the region which would direct the particles freed from the structural bonds at the leading surface and result in their travelling through the whole region to take up positions in the lattice behind the region. The particles have very high speeds in their orbits with the lattice at the space frequency. Once released they can travel at such speed through the lattice to their new positions. Their momentum will balance the forward momentum of the whole region. Their population would be small for motions at normal galactic speeds and so they would not distort the lattice sufficiently to affect the analysis presented in earlier chapters. For example, as they travel at $\frac{1}{2}c$ in the opposite direction to a lattice which may move at, say, 300 km/s, there would be one freely moving particle amongst 500 lattice particles. The lattice distortion in such a case would be very local to the free particle and elsewhere the lattice would comply with the analysis for the undisturbed system.*

This is the simple answer to the Michelson–Morley experiment. The E-frame moves linearly with the Earth. The effects described cannot be detected magnetically because the reverse flow of free lattice particles relative to the E-frame is exactly balanced electromagnetically by the continuum charge within the region. This charge is at rest but relative to the lattice structure of the E-frame it also has a reverse motion.

Thus the linear motion is very elusive in manifesting effects physically, though the Michelson–Morley experiment is hardly inconsequential. It is only because relativity has cast such a large cloud over the subject that this basic experiment is insufficient by itself to give endorsement to the structured space model advanced in this work. Nevertheless, when we consider the rotation of the lattice region we have a different story. Angular momentum effects and magnetic effects come in evidence and have no counterpart relativistic explanation. Then bear in mind that under certain conditions, seemingly stimulated by charge polarization in matter, the lattice can share the rotation of a material body.

As the Earth rotates its space lattice rotates with it. This induces charge polarization throughout the Earth's body and atmosphere and is balanced, as we saw in explaining the geomagnetic field, by charge polarization in the substance of the Earth itself. Now, what happens when a body of matter on Earth, such as a flywheel rotates? It cannot induce rotation of the space lattice by mere mechanical means. It needs the charge polarization to encourage rotation and a very high concentration of charge would be needed to cause rotation at the

---

* The existence of free lattice particles may affect the theoretical evaluation of the fine structure constant. See discussion of this in Appendix III.

speeds we associate with the flywheel. However, it could have an effect, because there is the residual polarization associated with the Earth's rotation. If it is the charge density that counts and the body occupied by the flywheel substance has charge to offset that of the Earth's rotating space lattice, then this same charge can be deployed to cause rotation of the space lattice within the flywheel to the extent that is exactly in balance with this charge.

Equation (228) tells us that the charge density is proportional to the speed of lattice rotation. Therefore, there would seem to be no change in the rotation of the lattice attributable to the motion of the flywheel, because the charge density is the same. However, equation (228) needs correction. It only applies if the axis of rotation of the whole lattice system is parallel to the universal axes about which the lattice particles describe their orbits. If there is an angle between these axes then the charge density is proportional to the cosine of this angle. The Earth's axis precesses at 23·5° about an axis that may more likely be in parallel with the universal axial direction in space in the vicinity of the solar system. Hence we may need to regard the Earth's space boundary as nearer 200 km above the Earth's surface to account quantitatively for the geomagnetic moment. This modification is, nevertheless, extremely relevant if our flywheel can determine the applicable axis for space lattice rotation within the body of the flywheel or in its near vicinity. If the wheel rotates about an axis in alignment with the universal axial direction in space then we see that the lattice in the body of the wheel need not rotate quite so rapidly to provide the charge balance. Indeed, it would slow down by about 10%, that is 10% of the rate of rotation of the Earth, a very small amount.

This theory may, therefore, give pointers to sensitive experiments which could be performed on rotating systems to see if there is a very small amount of angular momentum exchange or electrical charge adjustment when rotation is initiated or stopped for different orientations of the rotation axis. This would be a most direct way of verifying the existence of the proposed space medium and determining the axial direction about which the lattice particles rotate.

Note that we are led from the analysis of the optical experiments by reference to Fig. 20 in Chapter 3 to suspect that there can be local rotation of space lattice in the presence of rotating apparatus. However, it would be absurd to suggest that the lattice could readily rotate at the full speed of rotation of the apparatus and pass undetected in our observations. Accordingly, there must be a mechanism limiting the rate of rotation under normal circumstances and the one proposed above seems the most logical. Equally, one should not exclude the prospect that it might be possible to induce rapid rotation of the space lattice under certain circumstances.

This raises all kinds of interesting questions. We have seen that an electrical charge induction within matter can stimulate the spin of the space lattice. Once spinning as a result of the deployment of this electrical energy, there is radial lattice particle displacement which generates a magnetic field and holds electric charge in matter in a compensating electric balance. The body and rotating space lattice will tend to stay together in their onward migration through space. Therefore, should it not be possible within the laboratory to establish the coupled rotation of a body and the coextensive space lattice? The answer must be affirmative and the consequence is that we have here basis for putting this theory to its test, possibly with practical consequences.

Let us examine the energy content of such a system. A sphere of the space medium of mass density ρ_0 (only evident in rotation and not evident in linear motion) is set in rotation at angular velocity w. It has a radius R. Its kinetic energy due to rotation has a density given by $\rho_0 w^2 R^2 / 5$ ergs/cc. We know that ρ_0 is 288 gm/cc. Thus the energy density is about $60v^2$ ergs/cc, where v is the velocity of the sphere at its perimeter. If v is of the order of the speed of sound or the speed of gas molecules in air at normal temperatures and pressures then this energy density becomes about $8 \ 10^{10}$ ergs/cc. This is $8 \ 10^9$ joules per cubic metre. If the rotating space medium were somehow to be created naturally in the atmosphere this is the energy density one might expect it to possess. Furthermore there would be some electric charge displacement which could involve ionization of the air in the spherical form of the object. As the object slowed down the energy could sustain such ionization for a while. The object would be in a balanced buoyant state and would display no inertia, except that due to its rotation, though it would stay with the rotating air which it has ionized. But how could it be created? It requires a radial electric field to induce the rotation, as we saw from the creation of the sun. Perhaps a lightning discharge involving pinch in the discharge channel due to its self-electrodynamic contraction could separate electrons and ions in a radial sense along the discharge path, at least for a long enough period to induce the spin. This is all speculation, but it is a fact that thunderballs produced in thunderstorms are spherical in form. They glow as if ionized but their energies are far in excess of that one associates with ionized air. This was discussed in *Nature** in 1970. So difficult is this question that the proposal was made that the thunderball is a nuclear phenomenon. From evidence presented in the paper the task is to explain why the thunderball has an energy density which is independent of its size and of the order of $2 \ 10^9 \ J \ m^{-3}$ to $5 \ 10^9 \ J \ m^{-3}$.

It is submitted that the phenomenon of ball lightning is a phenomenon of the space medium. The scope for applying ball lightning to practical ends was discussed by Ritchie† as long ago as 1963. However, it can hardly be applied unless the mechanism underlying its creation is understood, as it is potentially destructive. In this connection the thunderball has been related to the vast destruction at Tunguska in 1908‡ when what appears to be a comet collided with the Earth and yet appeared to impart no momentum able to leave a crater. Comets themselves have weird properties which resemble the characteristics of the rotating space medium presented in this work, but it is beyond our scope to enlarge on such a theme.

Within the laboratory there is evidently scope for seeking to induce what may be termed 'vacuum spin'. An electrical or magnetic coupling is needed and there is scope for tapping some of the angular momentum of the space medium. Thus any experiment in which there appears anomalous torque deserves more serious attention than one would think. One example of such an experiment is that reported by Zinsser§ in 1975.

There is another phenomenon which involves unusual angular momentum properties. It is the mysterious mechanism of the tornado. It has been argued very convincingly by Vonnegut** that the energy of a tornado comes from the electrical discharges we associate with thunderstorms but that there is mystery in the source of the very substantial angular momentum of the tornado. Vonnegut speculates that the energy somehow concentrates the angular momentum of an ordinary whirlwind and, of particular interest in view of the foregoing comments, he goes on to make two statements:

* M. D. Altschuler *et al.*, *Nature*, **228**, 545 (1970).
† D. J. Ritchie, *Journal of I.E.E.*, **9**, 202 (1963).
‡ J. Stoneley, *Tunguska*, W. H. Allen, London (1977).
§ R. G. Zinsser, 'Kinetobarische Effekte—ein neues Phänomen?', *Umschau*, **5**, 152 (1975).
** B. Vonnegut, *Jour. Geophysical Research*, **65**, 203 (1960).

. . . it is possible that the vortex is initiated directly by electrical energy . . . an understanding of ball lightning may very well be necessary if the tornado puzzle is to be solved.

We see from this that the space medium may provide many of the missing answers needed to complete our understanding of the enigma we regularly encounter in physics.

The Hadron Ether

The author's first publication* showing the structured space medium described in developed form in the previous chapters appeared in 1960. The fine structure constant, the geomagnetic field and reference to the basic law of electrodynamics in the context of gravitation were the prime features. Years later, the author found that this basic form of electrodynamic law could have been extracted from Maxwell's treatise, but in pursuing the subject in ignorance of this there was advantage in discovering the more general law applicable between ions and electrons. Nevertheless, it was in this early 1960 publication that the need for the space medium to contain lattice particles of mass $3 \cdot 7 \ 10^{-29}$ gm was firmly asserted. In the second edition of the work published in 1966 the theory had been extended. The vacuum model then assumed the form outlined in this book. Space itself contained particles of mass energy $2 \cdot 587$ Gev constituting a G-frame which was in balance with a frame comprising the lattice particles. It was recognized then that these latter particles had an energy attributable to twice their effective mass, owing to the 'buoyancy' of the sea of energy pervading space. Thus the energy of these lattice particles is about 38 kev. The muon and the electron were seen as intermediate leptons between these two energy quanta in space, the $2 \cdot 587$ Gev quantum and the 38 kev quantum.

This was in the 1966 version of the author's published theory. Having deduced the need for the $2 \cdot 587$ Gev particle as the key to the derivation of the value of G, the author did look for support in the scientific literature of the time. There was, indeed, some speculation in 1966 about the existence of a really fundamental heavy particle which might decay to form elementary particles. Of special interest was the fact that evidence of parity breaking and a violation of Lorentz invariance in the decay of the kaon led to guarded assertions

* H. Aspden, *The Theory of Gravitation*, Sabberton, Southampton (1960).

that there might have to be an aether after all. Something in the vacuum was reacting with matter in high energy experiments. A link with gravitation was even suggested by Phillips* writing under the title 'Is the Graviton a Goldstone Boson?' This greatly encouraged the author and stimulated the 1966 publication, in spite of the hostile climate of opinion against proposals founded upon analysis of the aether medium.

The problem, it seemed, was that gravitation was the realm of the relativist to whom the aether is an anathema, whereas the particle physicist is intimately concerned with experimental data and its empirical formulation and can speak about 'broken symmetry' without colouring the argument by reference to the aether.

In any event, as the reader will have seen, the scope for progress turned out to be more in the realm of particle physics than in the cosmological terrain of relativity. But what is the progress towards recognizing the basic aether particle forms at 2·587 Gev and 38 kev? In particular, what is the progress in recognizing that the 2·587 Gev quantum is the graviton? This book has been written to stimulate thought in such a direction. There is independent progress, judging by the papers being published at the present time.

Bardeen and Tye† have written about the scope for a new light Higgs boson of approximate mass energy 50 kev. The Salam–Weinberg model is their base. Matsuki‡ has written about the effects of the Higgs scalar on gravity and speaks of the strong graviton proposed by Salam. Such a graviton has a mass energy measured as a few Gev. However, the methods of these authors differ greatly from the semi-classical methods used by the author in this work.

Occasionally, one does see direct reference to the hadronic aether. Koshiba§ writing in 1975 used a title including the words 'Does Hadronic Ether Exist?' Bailey and Picasso** in their 1970 paper on the anomalous magnetic moment of the muon referred to the hypothetical leptonic boson which had been predicted to exist in the field medium in order to explain slight differences between the theoretical and experimental g-factors for the electron and the muon. A mass of the leptonic boson of about 3·8 Gev was predicted. This was, of course, well before the discovery of the psi particles, but, as was

* P. R. Phillips, *Physical Review*, **146**, 966 (1966).
† W. A. Bardeen and S. H. H. Tye, *Physics Letters*, **74B**, 229 (1978).
‡ T. Matsuki, *Progress Theor. Phys.*, **59**, 235 (1978).
§ M. Koshiba, *Jour. Phys. Soc. Japan*, **38**, 305 (1975).
** J. Bailey and E. Picasso, *Progress in Nuclear Physics*, **12**, 62 (1970).

explained in Chapter 6, there has been mounting evidence indicating that certain heavy particle forms were needed to complete the picture of elementary particle interactions.

Importance of Unification

The idea of providing a unified account of gravitation and electrodynamic interactions has been recognized as important in physics for more than one hundred years. It is an obvious step towards the simplification of our understanding of Nature's fundamental fabric. In recent decades the mysteries of elementary particle physics have been deemed to be linked to the further progress in solving this basic problem of unification. But why is it important? Certainly, it is a challenge for enquiry by the theoretical physicist and progress towards a solution will put existing knowledge of physics on a firmer basis. This apart, the solution may lead us to valuable knowledge of practical importance, knowledge which otherwise we may not acquire. What, therefore, has been achieved in this book and why is this of importance?

Hopefully, the reader has come to believe in the possibility that there is a structured aether which regulates the values of the fundamental physical constants. This has academic value. Hopefully, also, the reader may have come to realize that the mysteries of the creation of our solar system are not necessarily outside our grasp. More knowledge of this kind is gratifying to our curiosity. Specifically, however, we have addressed the problem of electrodynamic interaction between current elements. It has been found that the magnetic field theory universally accepted has its limitations. Its valid application is restricted to problems involving at least one closed circuit interaction, and then only if the current carriers have the same charge/mass ratio. Magnetic field theory was based upon phenomena related exclusively to electron currents. What, then, is so special about interactions involving charged particles of different charge/mass ratio? Where is the practical application for such knowledge?

The answer may well coincide with the answer to the question: 'What is the most urgent and most important technological problem of our time?' Fusion power. Our attempts to emulate the energy generation processes of the sun by triggering fusion in heavy isotopes of hydrogen. Early efforts concentrated on techniques of magnetic confinement by which energy was concentrated to a critical level required for the nuclear reaction. All these efforts have been thwarted by instabilities of the electrical arc discharge which should self-pinch to concentrate the energy and impart this energy to the ions of the fusion process. This whole process is concerned with the transfer of energy from electrons to ions. Interactions between charged particles of different charge/mass ratio are vital to this fusion process. Yet, if we have inadequate understanding of the electrodynamic laws, as suggested in this work, is it surprising that progress has been retarded?

Another approach to fusion power is that of inertial confinement. This depends upon the injection of energy by accelerated particle beams. A recent review of progress is presented in the November, 1978, issue of *Scientific American* at p. 50. Electron beams and, it is stated, ion beams, are now being considered in the experimental attempts to stimulate fusion. Here, one may run into the problems of the anomalous acceleration of ions now evident in some experiments. It is proving very difficult to explain how energy is transferred from electrons to ions in the plasma experiments being performed. Indeed, there is mounting evidence that something is wrong with the laws of electrodynamics which we suppose regulate the interactions between electrons and ions. The author has drawn attention to this evidence in a recent publication* and argued that the true law of electrodynamics is the one derived in Chapter 1, as also published in a 1969 journal.†

It is submitted, therefore, that progress towards fusion power can be aided by a more rapid understanding of the fundamental physics involved in electrodynamic interactions. Here, then, the ideas in this book do assume practical importance. More than this, however, there is the suggestion in the foregoing pages that the phenomenon of the thunderball might be explicable and that from such understanding one might be able to control the storage of energy in the vacuum itself. Perhaps such an energized object could be propelled into a thermonuclear reactor and caused to release its energy to trigger the fusion reaction? But how can such ideas be explored if one does not admit the phenomenon on which they are founded? Belief in the aether medium is essential to such research, and it is interesting to read that the study of ball lightning has already been encouraged in USSR in connection with thermonuclear research. Kapitsa's

---

* H. Aspden, *IEEE. Trans. Plasma Science*, **PS-5**, 159 (1977).
† H. Aspden, *Jour. Franklin Inst.*, **287**, 181 (1969).

investigations in this context is reviewed in the 1977 work *Lightning*, edited by R. H. Golde and published by Academic Press (see Chapter 12).

Finally, on another note underlying the importance of enquiry into the aether medium, one should keep in mind the close connection between the gravitational stability of matter and the electric polarization of the rotating space medium suggested in this book. Here may be the means for developing the link between the earthquake and the unusual electric phenomena often associated with earthquakes. These take the form of lightning displays sometimes occurring in advance of the actual earthquake. Also it is reported that radio interference can exhibit certain anomalous features immediately prior to the earthquake[*] and there has been speculation about whether the monitoring of radio interference could give early warning of earthquakes and so help avert disaster.[†] It may, therefore, be of great importance for mankind to reconsider his scientific doctrines and re-examine the scope for a revival of the aether in the active vocabulary of physics.

[*] M. Markert, *New Scientist*, **70**, 488 (1976).
[†] R. E. Hill, 'The Radioquake Mystery', *Intercom*, 17, December, 1978; and H. Aspden, 'A Perspective on a New Enigma', *Intercom*, 21, December, 1978.

APPENDIX I

Uniform Charge Induction in a Self-gravitating Electron-Proton Gas

Consider an electron-proton gas in which unit volume contains N protons of charge e and mass m_p and n electrons of charge $-e$ and mass m_e. Imagine a state of equilibrium which renders the electrodynamic interactions negligible compared with the predominant electric interactions and, owing to the large scale nature of the system, the gravitational interactions.

The equilibrium condition implies uniform mass density ρ within the gas. It also implies zero net force on unit volume of electrons and protons due to the collective action of gravitation and the induced electric field. Hence, if the electric field intensity acting on this unit volume is V and the gravitational field intensity is g, we have:

$$V(Ne - ne) + g(Nm_p + nm_e) = 0 \qquad (239)$$

Note that by writing σ as the electric charge density this equation can be reformulated thus:

$$V\sigma + g\rho = 0 \qquad (240)$$

Since the gravitational force is attractive for mutual interaction we see from (240) that the electric interaction force must be repulsive. At radius x in a spherically symmetrical system we find that V is given by:

$$V = (1/x^2) \int_0^x 4\pi x^2 \sigma dx \qquad (241)$$

Similarly g is given in terms of the Constant of Gravitation G as:

$$g = - G(1/x^2) \int_0^x 4\pi x^2 \rho dx \qquad (242)$$

The uniformity of ρ assured by the thermodynamic equilibrium then allows (242) to be evaluated as:

$$g = -\frac{4\pi}{3} G\rho x \qquad (243)$$

From (240) and (243) we obtain:

$$V\sigma = \frac{4\pi}{3}G\rho^2 x \qquad (244)$$

From (241) and (244) we then obtain:

$$(\sigma/x^2)\int_0^x x^2\sigma dx = G\rho^2/3 \qquad (245)$$

Bearing in mind that ρ is constant, it is evident from (245) that σ must also be constant within the system, as may be verified by seeking to solve (245) by substituting arbitrary values of σ in terms of x. It follows from (245) that:

$$\sigma^2 = G\rho^2 \qquad (246)$$

This means that an electron-proton gas subject to predominant self electric and gravitational interactions will have a uniform intrinsic charge density and a uniform mass density related by equation (246). If the gaseous system has a total mass M then it will also have a charge Q given by:

$$Q = G^{\frac{1}{2}}M \qquad (247)$$

It may be wondered whether this would apply to a gas composed of hydrogen atoms. Such a gas has closely bound electrons and protons and is neutral in the main. Here there is the probability that there will be a small amount of ionization and the charge-mass ratio of the proton is so very large compared with that given by equation (247) above. Therefore the equation can be satisfied by a very small amount of ionization.

APPENDIX II

The Angular Momentum of the Solar System

In the following table the parameters from which the angular momenta of the planets can be estimated are listed. To simplify the data the planetary orbits are deemed to be circular. The data is in earth units, the mass, Earth orbit radius and annual rate of revolution in orbit being taken as reference. The sun, with an estimated angular momentum, is included to facilitate summation. All the angular momenta are in the same direction as all planets rotate in the same sense as the sun rotates about its axis.

Body	Mass	Orbit radius	Year/rev.	Angular momentum
Sun	332800	——	——	20 approx.
Mercury	0·05	0·387	0·24	0·03
Venus	0·82	0·723	0·62	0·69
Earth	1·00	1·00	1·00	1·00
Mars	0·11	1·52	1·88	0·135
Jupiter	317·8	5·20	11·86	724·6
Saturn	95·2	9·54	29·46	294·1
Uranus	14·5	19·18	84·01	63·5
Neptune	17·2	30·07	165	94·3
Pluto	0·11	39·44	248	0·69

The total angular momentum of the solar system may be estimated by summing the last column. It is found to be about 1200 Earth units. The Earth mass is approximately $6·0 \times 10^{27}$ gm and the Earth's orbital radius is approximately $1·5 \times 10^{13}$ cm. The Earth rotates in orbit through 2π radians in a year comprising $3·15 \times 10^{7}$ sec. Thus one Earth unit of angular momentum is $2·7 \times 10^{47}$ gm cm²/sec. 1200 such units makes the total angular momentum of the solar system some $3·2 \times 10^{50}$ gm cm²/sec.

It was stated in the main text when deriving equation (213) that this angular momentum would be substituted for X in:

$$X = 2MR^2w/5 \qquad (248)$$

to deduce an estimated value of the sun's angular velocity w before it ejected the planets. The sun's mass M would be very slightly greater than its present value of 1.989×10^{33} gm and its radius would be little different from its present value of 6.96×10^{10} cm. Thus we find that w can be estimated as somewhat less than the value of 8.3×10^{-5} rad/sec obtained by direction substitution of these figures.

APPENDIX III

The Fine Structure Constant

In the discussion of moving E-frames in Chapter 9 it was suggested that linear motion of the space lattice implied a reverse motion of free lattice particles at their speed $\frac{1}{2}c$ in orbit in the E-frame. Thus, for a motion through space at 390 km/s (or $\frac{1}{2}c/385$), as measured from the analysis of isotropic cosmic background radiation, we expect to see one free lattice particle in reverse motion per 385 lattice particles in the E-frame.

Consider now the motion of particles as suggested by Fig. 36 in Chapter 7. The lattice particles in E-frame orbit are not changing state during their motion and they are, therefore, in the contracted state intermediate states A and B. When they become free and move through the lattice they are subject to the same cyclic changes of state as other particles. Their β factor, or energy as referenced on their rest state, and as discussed by reference to Fig. 36, is that applicable to the speed $\frac{1}{2}c$ or 1·154. Since the radius of a lattice particle is inversely proportional to its energy, its volume in the rest state is $(1·154)^3$ times that in its state of motion with the E-frame. This is an increase of 0·54 of the volume of the lattice particle when freed from the E-frame. The base volume is 1/5060 that of a unit cell of the lattice. Accordingly, the effect of linear lattice motion at 390 km/s causes the volume available for continuum on a per E-frame lattice particle basis to diminish by one part in 5060 times 385 divided by 0·54 or by the factor 2·8 10^{-7}. This affects the equality of (133), effectively decreasing d^3 and thereby effectively increasing the 32π factor in (134) in the same proportion. In its turn, this increases the value of α^{-1} derived in (157) by 2·8 parts in 10^7. The resulting evaluation is 137·035953, an important change, especially as α^{-1} is now being measured to accuracy of this order (see footnote on p. 112).

EPILOGUE

In the opening words of Chapter 1 there were quotations from the book *The Universe and Dr. Einstein* authored by Lincoln Barnett. Now, having reached the end of this work *Physics Unified*, it seems appropriate to quote further from Barnett's book:

If the fullest implications of a Unified Field Theory are sustained by the tests of the future—if the laws of quantum physics can also be derived from its equations—crucial new insights will doubtless be attained into the composition of matter, the structure of the elementary particles, the mechanics of radiation, and other enigmas of the subatomic world. Yet these will be essentially by-products. For the great philosophical triumph of any Unified Field Theory is implicit in the first word of its title. It will carry to logical fulfillment the long course of science towards the unification of man's concepts of the physical world.

INDEX